*THE SEXUALLY
RESPONSIVE WOMAN*

THE
SEXUALLY
RESPONSIVE
WOMAN

Phyllis and Eberhard
KRONHAUSEN

Preface by
SIMONE DE BEAUVOIR

GROVE PRESS, INC.   NEW YORK

Contents

Contents

Preface

THE Doctors Kronhausen have written a forthright, courageous, and highly rigorous study on the difficult problem of women's sexuality, about which so little is known. They have gone further and called into question even that which has hitherto been regarded as an unalterable fact of Nature: woman's "physiological destiny." In this realm as in so many others, male prejudice insists on keeping woman in a state of dependency. In contrast to this, the authors grant her an autonomy—both physiological and psychological—equal to that of man.

I am not qualified to pass definite judgment on all the findings and conclusions of the Doctors Kronhausen. On the whole, however, the wide range of documentation as well as their precise and subtle analyses are thoroughly convincing.

Quite aside from this, I have found *The Sexually Responsive Woman* truly absorbing and fascinating reading. I can only hope that a piece of work such as this will be widely read and stimulate many more analyses aimed at overcoming the myths and clichés with which we are only too easily satisfied.

The authors have done much to set the facts in their true light. My personal sympathies and best wishes are on their side.

—*Simone de Beauvoir*

By Way of Explanation

To acquaint the reader with the structure of this book, we feel a brief explanation might be in place.

In the opening section of this study, we wish to draw attention to the need for and importance of a better understanding of female sexuality. We shall consider this problem from the point of view of individual happiness, social progress, and mental health.

In order to place our discussion on the soundest scientific basis, we are introducing the reader to the latest research in the new science of reproductive human biology concerned with the anatomy and physiology of woman's sex response. Realizing that this particular aspect of human sexuality, important as it is, lies somewhat beyond our own professional field, we shall restrict ourselves to reporting on these findings and relating them to other scientific data.

In addition, we are examining the psychoanalytic literature so as to present a critical review of Freudian and post-Freudian theories regarding female sexuality.

Having taken these preliminary steps, we will develop our own theories concerning woman's sex response and erotic potential by quoting from the actual sex histories of some of the women we have interviewed for this purpose.

Our approach to this subject is not a statistical one, though we did interview a large number of American and European women in connection with their sex response. Instead, we employed the methods most congenial to our way of working, namely the *psychological depth interview* and *content analysis*.

From the group of volunteers who co-operated in our project by giving us their sex histories, we have selected a small number of women—four in all—of very different personal dispositions and social background. It is their sexual experiences, attitudes, and relationships which we are examining at close range and in every relevant detail in order to arrive at a new and fuller understanding of woman's sex responses.

In addition we are attempting, from the various impressions gained in the course of our investigations, to make some predictions concerning the future of female sexuality as we see it evolving.

PART I

I

Truth and Fiction about Women

THERE is no topic on earth which has produced as much written nonsense, both learned and not-so-learned, as that of female sexuality; and yet, for all its popularity as a subject of conversation from barroom to lecture hall, the image of woman as a sexual being has not become more clearly perceived nor better understood.

According to one ancient tradition, woman puts on the attitudes of coyness and reticence only to conceal an insatiable sexual greed and lasciviousness, an extreme reaction in the minds of certain ascetic males to whom female sexuality always has and always will represent an immense potential danger. It is this attitude which has given rise to the myth of woman as the *eternal temptress* (the Eve of Paradise) and, in its less flattering guises, of the medieval witch, riding on her broomstick to nocturnal orgies; of the blood-sucking vampire, weakening or killing her male victims in their sleep; of the predatory whore, always on the prowl for erotic adventure and sexual gratification.

Diametrically opposed to this negative vision of woman as the incorporation of vegetative sexuality steaming with erotic desire, there is the equally ancient myth of woman as the *eternal virgin*, the sexless mother, the untouchable saint who through her spiritual purity raises and ennobles the grosser, baser male. It is from this sexless type of mother-figure that man may expect protection, deliverance, and the fulfillment of his infantile and dependent needs—provided he does not make a sexual approach to her.

What truth, if any, one may ask, can there be in these opposing historical views of women?

We are inclined to think there may be justifiable foundation in fact for both of them. Behind the myth of woman as the eternal temptress there seems to linger the suspicion that she may yet turn out to be the more highly sexed member of the human species. And, as far as the sexless virgin myth is concerned, it may be based on the observation that it is possible for woman to completely split off in her mind the erotic from the reproductive aspects of sexuality—a capacity which constitutes one of the few genuine psychological sex differences that is *not* culturally induced.

These are the two sides of the coin, with the image of the predatory Messalina on the one side, and the spiritualized virgin-mother on the other; both concepts of woman containing some degree of truth, but both equally unrealistic in their extremes.

Looking at it from a historical viewpoint, it seems that the myth of woman as the eternal temptress had preceded that of the sexless virgin by a long space of time, until the pendulum of popular prejudice swung all the way in the opposite direction. "It would appear," says Havelock Ellis, speaking of pre-World War I conditions, "that whereas in earlier ages there was generally a tendency to credit women with an unduly large share of the sexual impulse, there is now a tendency unduly to minimize the sexual impulse in women." Adding the space of another generation to this time perspective, to bring it up to date, we can see how the concept of womanhood has been gradually approaching a more balanced image in which the motherly, sexual, and erotic aspects of femininity are no longer seen as mutually contradictory qualities, but as complementary aspects of the female character.

It is, however, undeniable that the notion of woman as

the lesser sexed of the sexes is still the dominant one in our society. This is all the less surprising when one realizes how deeply embedded in Western, and even in Western scientific, thought the de-sexed concept of woman really is.

Only a couple of generations ago, Acton, who was considered the greatest authority on sexual matters in England, was able to say that "happily for society[!]" the idea that women possess sexual feelings could be put aside as "a vile aspersion." Another medical sage of that period declared that obvious sex interest or desire "only happens in lascivious women."

And scarcely a generation ago, the greatest sexologist of the day, the much-quoted Krafft-Ebing, said of woman that, "if she is normally developed mentally and well-bred, her sexual desire is small. If this were not so, the whole world would become a brothel and marriage and a family impossible. It is certain, that the man that avoids women and the woman that seeks men are abnormal."

The logical correlate to this way of thinking was that, since women were said to be subject to lesser sexual desire, they did not really require much sexual gratification either —an attitude which was taken over by the women themselves and which was prevalent until rather recently. It found expression in the sexually resigned wife who felt that her own erotic needs did not count, just as long as *he* "had his pleasure."

For such a point of view there seemed to be ample corroboration from the life of sub-human species in nature— with the picture of the placid cow, chewing away peacefully during coitus with the wildly excited bull, as the classical prototype. Or the laboratory experiment, favorite with beginning psychology students, in which the female of a pair of copulating rats will invariably go for a piece of cheese, put in front of them, while the male never yields to the call of the stomach over that of his gonads.

So impressive is this sort of evidence from nature that

even Freud, and to some extent apparently also Kinsey, were not free from its influence. Freud, as one may recall, felt that all libido or sexual energy was essentially *male*—a theory which, as we shall see, led to much confusion in psychoanalytic thinking and to serious errors in clinical practice. Kinsey, on the other hand, if we understand him correctly, was led by the same route of reasoning (from analogy in nature) to the conviction that women (or at least two-thirds of them) were *innately* less capable of responding to psychological sex stimuli than men.

In support of this theory, women's lesser interest in the nude figure and a variety of other psychological sex stimuli from burlesque to erotic writings and erotic art are frequently cited as corroborating evidence. From these, on the surface, self-evident facts, the suggestive, but not necessarily correct inference is often drawn that women respond as "touch animals" primarily to direct physical rather than mental stimulation.

Hand in hand with these dubious notions about female sexuality, there have arisen two further myths about women's sex response: one, the *vaginal orgasm* theory, grew directly out of the initial Freudian error of the supposedly "male" libido which was said to be centered in the clitoris, and which made that organ suspect in psychoanalytic thinking because of its anatomical resemblance to the male sex structure; the other myth concerns the idea that women are *slower* in their sex response than men, an observation which has frequently been linked with the previously mentioned one that women's sex response seems to be largely limited to physical stimulation, without the benefit of the same degree of psychological excitation as in the male.

Unfortunate as these old and new misconceptions about women (which so seductively recommend themselves to "common sense") may be in terms of individual unhappiness and frustration, their social ramifications are still more damaging and deplorable. Among the social evils which they

and their medieval precursors have brought in train, there
looms large the pernicious double standard in sexual ethics
which has been perpetuated from generation to generation
into our own time. According to that mode of thinking,
a socially disapproved sex act may be permissible if committed by a male, but not necessarily so if perpetrated by a
female. In other words, the assumption that women are subject to less urgent sexual needs than men has been taken as
justification for stricter social control of their sexual conduct.

In keeping with this proposition, Western society has
traditionally been protective toward women only with regard
to the *reproductive* side of sex, but punitive with respect to
its *erotic* aspects. At the same time, the supposed sexual
inferiority of women (for that is what all the theories,
ancient and modern, about women's alleged lesser sexuality
and superior "spirituality" in the end amounted to in the
popular mind) came to be used as a redundant argument to
justify discrimination against them in non-sexual areas as
well (e.g., in employment and in the curtailment of political
rights).

The way this sort of thing has worked against equal employment opportunities for women can, for instance, be seen
from an observation of the U.S. Supreme Court in the year
1869, upholding the refusal of the Illinois State Bar to admit
a woman lawyer, with the argument that "the natural
and proper timidity and delicacy which belong to the female
sex evidently unfit it for many of the occupations of civil
life." On the other hand, the fact that women themselves
have taken over these social prejudices to their own detri-
ment is well illustrated by the statement of a woman lawyer
who recently told a *Time* magazine reporter that she remembered two girls being eliminated at her law class, "because they just could not bring themselves to argue a case of
rape."

An even more direct example of legal discrimination
against women on the basis of the double standard has been

brought to public attention in Europe in 1961 by the news coverage of two adultery cases in Italy.

In that country, the law provides for a different treatment of adultery, depending on whether it is committed by the wife or by the husband. If the adultery is committed by a wife, it is a crime punishable by imprisonment. If committed by the husband, it can be punished only if he keeps a mistress in his own house, or "in a public and notorious way."

This flagrantly discriminatory law had never been challenged until the lawyers for two female defendants in adultery cases took the matter to Italy's highest tribunal, the Constitutional Court. They argued that the law under which the women had been convicted was in violation of the Italian Constitution which incorporates the principle of non-discrimination between the sexes.

After pondering the matter, the (naturally all-male) Constitutional Court came up with the following involuntary self-revelation: it held that the law was justified in treating adultery committed by a wife more severely because "in conformity with the *common opinion*" it "constituted objectively a more serious offence."

In an attempt to justify their opinion the learned judges explained that the law was aiming at protecting the *unity of the family* (read, the *patriarchal family*); and such a unity was more seriously threatened by a wife's adultery than by a husband's.

Instances of this nature make it unmistakably clear why the idea of female sex equality ceases to be of purely theoretical concern to social conservatism: if applied in practice it would spell the end of a social order based on the *patriarchal* family. Any serious criticism of the patriarchal family structure, such as emphasis on the erotic rights of women implies, is therefore automatically interpreted by a threatened conservatism not only as a moral issue, but also as a form of political *subversion*.

A clearer recognition of the true nature of female sexuality is, however, badly needed if we are to develop a new sex ethos which is in keeping with the realities of the matter and adequate to help us cope with the social problems confronting society.

There is no doubt that woman's potentiality in orgasm not only equals, but actually surpasses that of the male, at least in one respect: woman's greater capacity for the experience of *multiple orgasm*. (Van de Velde: "The woman . . . can . . . reach orgasm . . . far more frequently than the man, so that it may be said that her sexual power, provided that the attraction is sufficiently strong, is much greater than his.")

The sex-history material which we have collected also suggests that woman's potential response to psychological aphrodisiacs is no less than that of man. The confusion on this issue has, in our opinion, arisen from misinterpreting the fact that women respond to *different* types of psychological sex stimuli than men and are socially conditioned to inhibit their sexual response to a far greater extent than is true for men. In contrast to most prevailing expert opinions on this point, we therefore suggest that none of the data indicate that women possess a lesser innate *capacity* for the appreciation of such mental aphrodisiacs—provided they take into account the different erotic interests of the sexes.

The same holds true with regard to the strength of women's over-all sex drive: cross-cultural studies and individual cases from our own society indicate very clearly that one cannot here speak of a genuine sex difference. What we do see (as Margaret Mead and other anthropologists have pointed out) is that societies which encourage women to respond sexually produce females who demonstrate a sexual impulse of equal strength to that of man. On the other hand, where society discourages or penalizes the manifestation of strong sexual desire in women, it produces females whose sexual impulse seems to be inferior to that of the male.

On the basis of these facts, we can only conclude that

contemporary Western society is behaving in an irrational and neurotic manner in continuing to believe ancient fables and myths about women in order to preserve a social *status quo* which is no longer functional to the requirements of modern life. Nor should it surprise one that the price we are all paying for this sort of rigidity and short-sightedness is high in exact proportion to the magnitude of the error committed.

To uphold the corroding patriarchal family structure, family life itself is put in danger; to preserve the concept of a totally unrealistic absolutism in the monogamy of marriage, the stability of marriage itself is put into jeopardy; men who want their women to be both "sexy" and virginal at the same time are frustrating not only their partners, but also themselves; women who insist on economic and political equality, but accept the double sex standard (based on the unspoken assumption of their sexual inferiority) find the doors to higher office and equal economic chances mysteriously barred; and society is deprived of the much greater potential contribution that women could make in every field of public and professional life.

At the same time, hostile sexual tensions, widespread discontent, and frustration on the part of both sexes are allowed to spread from their original focus in the traditional marriage situation into other areas of public life, poisoning it, so to speak, at its very source. The reason for this is that sexuality cannot be isolated from the rest of social life, nor can the personal misery resulting from sexual confusion, misinformation, and outdated marriage arrangements be quarantined so that it will not infect other aspects of our culture which seem unrelated to sexuality.

This point of view is shared by many responsible social scientists who have expressed fears that sexual frustrations and unhappiness in the marriage situation may have an unfortunate *radiation effect* into other areas of human relations as well. Dr. Hartshorne summarizes, for instance, the opinions of three social scientists, Chisholm, Saul, and Appel, in these words:

> It is interesting to conjecture whether this complex rejection, frustration, and anxiety-producing behavior experienced within the personal interrelationship of marriage may not be projected by the individuals who undergo it into the national and international scene, and so contribute to the type of aggressive behavior which is threatening society.

For these unhealthy and potentially dangerous social conditions we maintain that the mistaken notion concerning female sexuality (with the resultant double sex standard and consequent sex hostility and frustration) is one of the major hidden infectious sources in the body of our society. We suggest therefore as the first step to remedy this unhealthy situation to replace the fictitious notions about female sexuality with such hard facts as the biological and social sciences are able to provide today. Only then can we hope that eventually our social attitudes toward women and their erotic rights and nature will also change in conformity with the new understanding gained. And this development, one may justifiably hope, should result in the improvement of social relations between the sexes, happier marriages, healthier, more stable, and more democratic family life, and the gradual drying up of at least one insidious source of social poisoning which may be causing all the more damage and human misery for having hitherto not been clearly recognized as the invidious troublemaker in human relations that we hold it to be.

II

Psychoanalysis and Woman's Sex Response

ACCORDING to Freud's theory, the child, whether male or female, undergoes certain stages of psychosexual development before reaching the stage of adult genital sexuality. These stages are said to be first, the *oral* stage, with the mouth as the focus of erotic pleasure. Next, the *anal* stage, with the rectum as the primary erotic pleasure zone. And last, the *phallic* phase, with the penis or the clitoris, respectively, being the center of the child's pleasurable sensations. The phallic phase occurs before the individual enters the state of full *genital* sexuality, after a latency period (roughly from six to twelve years) in which the sex drive is said to be relatively dormant.

Freud thought that the child directed his sexual response first narcissistically toward himself, then homosexually toward the same sex, and finally heterosexually toward the opposite sex. This, Freud felt to be equally true for the male and the female child.

Much confusion has arisen from a too literal interpretation of these stages of psychosexual development which were meant to be no more than hypothetical constructions. But to later researchers, even such a hypothetical division seemed all too arbitrary.

Taking their point of departure from the actual sex behavior of children, psychologists have found that children are as likely to respond heterosexually as they are homosexually.

In other words, Freud's hypothesis that psychosexual development proceeds in a more or less regulated sequence from narcissistic masturbatory interests to homosexual and then to heterosexual interests was not proved by the direct observation of children. Recent research has also shown that the child's sexual interest really does not decline during the so-called latency period prior to the onset of adolescence, but that the child by then has simply learned to hide it more effectively.

Of the greatest importance to the problem of female sexuality, however, was Freud's view that during the phallic phase of psychosexual development, both boys and girls no longer focus on the mouth or anus as the prime source of erotic pleasure, but on the phallic part of their sexual apparatus—the clitoris of the girl and the penis of the boy. In addition, Freud considered the girl's clitoris as essentially an "atrophied penis," a notion which he also imputed to the little girl and which he thought to have unfortunate psychological repercussions for her: she was, he figured, going to think of herself as really nothing more than a "littler boy," who had literally come too short by nature's caprice.

As she grows up, Freud thought, the girl has to transfer these pleasurable sensations from the clitoris to the vagina which she is to discover later on. As Freud wrote: "In the phallic phase of the girl, the clitoris is the dominant erotogenic (pleasure-giving) zone. But it is not destined to remain so; with the change of femininity, the clitoris must give up to the vagina its sensitivity, and with it, its importance, either wholly, or in part."

And elsewhere Freud stated: "The clitoris in the girl, moreover, is in every way equivalent during childhood to the penis. . . . In the transition to womanhood very much depends upon the early and complete relegation of this sensitivity from the clitoris over to the vaginal orifice."

Freud himself was not entirely happy with his own theory of woman's psychosexual development. He expressed the hope that some day female analysts would be "better able to apprehend the facts with greater ease and clearness, because they had the advantage of being suitable mother-substitutes in the transference situation with patients whom they were studying."

But instead of providing the hoped-for corrections, most of Freud's female disciples have contented themselves with a blind worship of the master.

Marie Bonaparte, for instance, devoted student and former analysand of Freud, merely amplified his emphasis by saying: "The ideal adaptation of woman to her erotic function involves the suppression of the . . . clitoris in favor of the vagina."

And Helene Deutsch, an equally famous student of Freud, said, "The competition of the clitoris, which intercepts the excitations unable to reach the vagina, and the genital trauma then create the dispositional basis of a permanent sexual inhibition, i.e., *frigidity*."

Psychoanalytic theory further assumes that in the course of growing up, the little girl comes to repudiate (reject) her mother who has been her first love object, because of her disappointment with her; in other words it is the girl's *penis envy* and *castration complex* which makes her unconsciously blame her mother. Under these influences, she supposedly gives up, or ought to give up, clitoral masturbation, become more passive, and turn to the father from whom she now expects a baby as a sort of consolation prize for the missing penis.

These changes are said to mark the famous *Oedipus complex*, which may persist well into adult life where it may cause any number of difficulties in the woman's sex life and marriage relations.

Freud believed further that strictly speaking there was, as we have already indicated, no feminine libido (sexual energy), inasmuch as the active, striving principle was essentially male and the female function inherently passive. He felt that Nature's aim of reproduction was best achieved through this particular arrangement and that the female who remained too active had not managed to conclude her feminine identification at the end of the "phallic phase." This developmental failure Freud considered the main cause of female frigidity, or, as he put it, "In those women who are sexually anaesthetic, as it is called, the clitoris has stubbornly retained this sensitivity."

If "explanations" such as these leave one rather dissatisfied and bewildered, one may find solace in Freud's own somewhat resigned comment, "If you want to know more about femininity, you must interrogate your own experience, or turn to the poets, or else wait until science can give you more profound and more coherent information."

Unfortunately, most of Freud's followers turned neither to the poets nor to science, but merely repeated the dogma according to Freud in one fashion or another.

No doubt Freud himself would have welcomed the new advances in our knowledge of sexual behavior made by such researchers as the Kinsey group. But the fact is that he did not have these at his disposal, nor the still more recent anatomical and physiological findings with regard to women's sex response which we shall discuss in the following chapter.

As matters stand today, clinicians of the ultra-Freudian school of psychoanalysis keep insisting that women who do not experience "vaginal orgasm" are by this definition "frigid" and "psychosexually immature." One cannot help feeling sorry for women patients who try to come up to the unrealistic expectations of therapists holding such beliefs. One of our female informants (the Married Lesbian), was such a case. She told us: "I've never had what they call *vaginal orgasm*, and I don't think I ever will. My poor analyst was periodically asking me whether I was having vaginal orgasm and I kept saying, 'I think it's getting better.' I couldn't bear to hurt his feelings."

Psychoanalysts of the orthodox school themselves seem to feel sorry for women; as one of them (Abraham Franzblau) put it: "In the human species the female gets a rough deal from nature in a number of ways. She has a far more difficult time attaining psychosexual maturity than the male. . . . Comparing the male and the female, we find that in contrast to her brother or husband there are five extra hurdles that the female has to overcome."

These obstacles which the woman has to scale, consist, according to this authority, of the following:

> 1st obstacle: the change in the site of sexual gratification (from clitoris to vagina); 2nd obstacle: the change in the love object (from mother to father); 3rd obstacle: the barrier of biology (menstruation—"One cannot ignore the fact that they [women] walk around bleeding for several days each month"); 4th obstacle: the human female is not subject to the powerful biological urge called *heat* . . . ("The female human being is historically a novice to pleasure"); 5th obstacle: the woman's dependency upon the man ("She needs a fully potent male for her gratification").

With women supposedly suffering from such an enormous natural handicap, one might well despair of ever seeing even one "psychosexually fully mature" female, as these clinicians refer to them, who has overcome all the unfair obstacles and won through. The only women who might qualify, we would have thought, would probably be the wives of the analysts themselves. Our disillusionment was, therefore, great when the wife of one of them, whom we interviewed for this study, complained bitterly to us about the capabilities of her analyst-husband as a lover. He had been depositing learned monographs and articles about female frigidity around the house for her to pick up hoping that she would take the hint. She took it—by finding a lover who did not believe in the "five obstacles"—and with whom she later led a very satisfactory sex life!

This woman, after twenty years of Freudian marriage, which was just then ending in divorce, gave us her considered opinion of the matter in a nutshell: with a seriousness which did not fail in its humorous effect, she pointed out, "It's not only the Belgian Congo that needs to be liberated, but the whole tribe of psychoanalysts' wives as well!"

Of course, we cannot agree with the doctrine of Nature's unfair discrimination against women. We now know, on the basis of such solid scientific research as is available, that there is no need for a shift or transfer of sensitivity from the clitoris to the vagina. On the contrary, it is not the vagina but the clitoris which remains throughout the woman's life the organ with the greatest potential for erotic stimulation. This is so because the clitoris has the greatest concentration of sensory nerve endings and a proportionately much greater erectile capacity than even the male penis.

Put differently, the vagina itself (and even the entrance to the vagina) has only relatively few sensory nerve endings, and seems to respond mainly to pressure; it may therefore provide an additional, though never the main stimulus to evoke the woman's sex response.

It has been shown by cross-cultural studies that the *Oedipus complex* with its accompanying *penis envy* and *castration complex* in the girl are not nearly as universal as early psychoanalytic thinkers had assumed them to be. Nor does the little girl necessarily have to fall madly in love with her father and come to hate her mother. In fact, there may not be an Oedipal stage with all its stormy conflicts and attendant misery for either the girl or boy, provided the cultural conditions are favorable for an alternative form of development.

Similarly, there is no reason to assume that biological sex differences and menstruation in particular put the woman at a disadvantage, unless the prevailing social attitudes bring this about.

Margaret Mead found that the women of Samoa did not even understand what she meant when she asked them whether or not they experienced pain or emotional difficulties in connection with their periods. Only one girl on the whole island knew what the anthropologist was talking about, and declared that she suffered from menstrual discomfort. This was the girl who was working for the local (white) missionary family!

And finally, with reference to the assertion that woman is supposed to be "historically a newcomer to pleasure," the situation is not as simple as these clinicians seem to assume. It is of course true, as we have already pointed out, that in most sub-human mammalian species the female does not seem to partake in the same kind of orgasmic experience as that represented by the ejaculation of the male. It is also possible that at one period in the dim pre-history of mankind, the human female may well have been similarly underprivileged in this respect. But even if this were so, man and woman have for scores of subsequent millennia developed their other attributes—why, then, should woman have failed to catch up with man in the realm of sex and sexual pleasure?

However, seeing woman at a prehistoric disadvantage is by no means the *only* way of looking at the problem. It is, for instance, not at all clear whether one is fully justified in equating the physiological phenomenon of ejaculation in the sub-human male with the *psychological* experience of human orgasm. As we know, ejaculation does not always spell orgasm in man, though it may be accompanied by some physiological tension release—of a kind, we must stress, which even on the purely physical level is not nearly as great and complete as when ejaculation and orgasm *do* coincide.

But since orgasm and ejaculation have several aspects in common and outwardly resemble each other, they have often been confused as being one and the same thing, which is, of course, not at all the case. One must keep this firmly in mind if one wants to avoid being seduced by faulty reasoning, and led to erroneous conclusions.

Also, if women were phylogenetically retarded, as these clinicians suggest, one would certainly expect the women in those primitive cultures which roughly represent an earlier stage in human development to show little interest in the erotic aspects of sexuality, and be more or less frigid. But this is, as we shall find, not at all the case (see "The Sociology of Orgasm").

Nevertheless, there are still many mysteries and unanswered questions about certain aspects of female sexuality; for instance, why is woman's sex drive not highest at the time of ovulation and greatest fertility instead of around the time of menstruation (when impregnation is almost impossible)? But to conclude from the present state of our knowledge that contemporary woman is at a genuinely erotic disadvantage seems to us totally unwarranted.

Some clinicians have allowed themselves to be carried away still farther from the realities of the matter. So much so, that they arrived at opinions which even the majority of their fellow-analysts considered untenable. Roheim, for instance, went so far as to speculate that "woman obtains real gratification only if after the sexual act she suffers from an *inflammation* of the genitals."

We could cite many more statements of this kind, each more absurd than the last, but we do not wish to imply that the clinicians who made them were or are cranks who need not be taken seriously. On the contrary, we are indebted to some of them for many of the most lucid psychological insights, and large numbers of patients who were treated by them undoubtedly owe their sanity to the efforts and skill of these clinicians.

For even though we have to point out the shortcomings, and even the undeniable psychological damage which has been caused by the fallacious reasoning of many Freudian analysts, we also wish to point to the fact that the overall impact of the psychoanalytic movement has still been one of enlightenment and liberation.

Moreover, the genius of Freud is often recognizable even in his errors, and we are far from trying to minimize his monumental achievement and benign impact on Western civilization by our criticism of his theory concerning female sexuality. It only goes to show to what extent even as brilliant a mind as his can be misled by the historical and sociological limitations of his time and cultural environment.

Also, the progressive school of psychoanalysts today takes greater account of the realities of female sexuality than the extreme examples of theoretical misconceptions which we have cited would indicate. For one thing, the anthropological and sociological schools of thought in America have greatly influenced the psychoanalytic movement, and more recently the Kinsey reports and other studies have had their effect on the thinking and practice of all but the most orthodox clinicians. In fact, it seems as though Freud's initial hope that some of his female students would make new and important contributions to the theory of female sexuality is finally being realized.

Of this second and third generation of psychoanalysts, female clinicians like Karen Horney, Clara Thompson, Phyllis Greenacre, and in England notably Melanie Klein, did much to bring psychoanalytic thinking up to date.

Clara Thompson frankly states:

> One of the weakest links in the Freudian thinking has been the explanation of the psychology of women. According to Freud, a woman is a castrated man, and most of her troubles arise from resentment of this. Implicit in the theory is the acceptance of the inferiority of women, and the task of the therapist is to make the woman reconciled to her fate and to make her willing to accept certain compensations for her lack of many assets. Thus, she may come in time to accept a child as a compensation for the lack of a penis.

After this criticism of orthodox Freudianism, she reaffirms her belief in a more optimistic state of affairs by saying: "It does not seem possible that half of the human race could have been born with a basic feeling of inferiority because of their anatomy and physiology."

The newer school of psychoanalysis also rejects the idea of

female *passivity* as against male *aggressiveness*. To quote again from Clara Thompson as one of the chief exponents of the new approach: "The use of the word 'passive' seems to me unfortunate and inaccurate. It implies that the female experience is the negative of the male. It seems more probable that the female's participation is of a different nature. She does not have to produce an erection, but, in another sense, she must be active. She must excite the male. Here, I am not talking of aggressiveness as seen in some neurotic behavior of women today, but the more subtle ways of making oneself desirable which seem to be the expression of the primitive attractiveness of women."

While the orthodox school of psychoanalysis laid stress on what were thought to be constitutionally determined psychological sex differences, the new school of psychoanalysis has tended to minimize these differences, or at least not to regard them as totally unalterable.

This view has been well expressed by Erich Fromm who largely draws upon sociological data for his original and challenging psychoanalytic theories. He writes: "It is apparent today that whatever differences exist between the sexes, they are relatively insignificant in comparison with the characterological differences that are found between persons of the same sex."

Some psychoanalysts are even attempting to reconcile the irreconcilable by mixing the latest biological findings on the female sex response with traditional psychoanalytic thinking. Of these, the most daring and outspoken is Judd Marmor, who in a recent article frankly admits that "the chief sensory area for erogenous sensation in women is localized in the glans clitoris, just as in men it is localized in the homologous (equivalent) glans penis. (The shaft of the penis, like the vagina, is lacking in genital corpuscles.)"

By this method of reasoning Dr. Marmor arrives at a conclusion which would seem identical with our own, namely that "strictly speaking there is no such thing as a *vaginal* orgasm in the female, any more than we might speak of *scrotal, anal* or *prostatic* orgasm in the male."

In the end, however, even that clinician, after a long and tortuous route of new theory-making, arrives at a position which to us seems indistinguishable from Freud's original point of departure. If the woman is "psychologically uninhibited," Dr. Marmor says, she will experience, "an intense orgastic response (to vaginal intercourse) in which the intromission of the phallus into the vagina is of major importance. This is both psychodynamically and physiologically the optimum type of response, and represents what is ordinarily characterized as a 'vaginal' orgasm."

A similar compromise position was taken by the Female Psychoanalyst whom we interviewed for the purpose of this study. It is true, her ideas on female sexuality were influenced by the newer, sociologically oriented school of psychoanalysis, but she too still maintained the *terminology* of *vaginal* and *clitoral* orgasm.

To our question as to whether she thought that there were two separate and distinct types of orgasm which a woman might experience, she said:

> No, I don't think there are two different kinds of orgasm. I am thinking of a clitoral and a vaginal orgasm, but I don't think they are totally different.
> I think that if women are very satisfied, they usually speak of contractions in the vagina. And if they have a masturbatory orgasm, or even sometimes an orgasm during intercourse, but without contractions in the vagina, they speak of it as a clitoral orgasm. Now I can't personally have vaginal orgasm, without some clitoral excitement, but I have had patients who said they do.

We think that this statement of our Female Psychoanalyst is fairly representative of the main current of present-day psychoanalytic thinking. It suggests that in psychoanalytic practice female patients are today less likely to be urged to achieve vaginal orgasm than had previously been the case. However, it also indicates the strong resistance on the part of clinicians toward abandoning a vocabulary which unfortunately creates much unnecessary confusion.

One can only hope that in the future the psychoanalytic movement will make better use of the most recent findings in the field of biological and behavioristic sciences. But really to profit from the assimilation of these facts, psychoanalytic theory-makers will have to undertake drastic revisions, instead of contenting themselves with halfway measures and ambiguous compromise solutions.

III

The Anatomy of Orgasm

THE female sex organs have never been a fashionable subject for scientific investigation. That, of course, is exactly why we have not known much about female sex anatomy until now.

Even in the eighteenth century, Linnaeus, in his great work *Systema Naturae* (1748), confessed that he had shuddered at the thought of having to direct his attention to an exact study of the female genitals. "Abominable," was the word he used, as he braced himself to overcome his natural reluctance, in the interests of science.

It is true that almost a century earlier, R. de Graef had attempted the same investigation in his famous treatise on the generative organs of women, *De Mulierum Organis Generationis Inservientibus*, (1672). But he too considered it necessary to apologize in the preface for the nature of his subject matter.

Even today, in this fact-minded age, research in this important branch of science has to be carried out under the cover of semi-secrecy and the camouflage of "reproductive biology." But what counts is that the work is being done and that most important findings are being made.

What these new and daring investigations into the anatomy and physiology of the female sex response have brought to light is truly amazing. And as we became immersed in the discoveries we began to realize that they were liable to completely change our concept not only of the physical, but also of the *psychological* aspects of female sexuality.

No speculation on the psychology of female sexuality has been fruitful without a sure and up-to-date understanding of its anatomy. It is equally important not to go *beyond* such knowledge in the making of theories.

This was the weakness of the Freudian system. Up to a point, Freud was correct. But the moment he ventured in his theory-making beyond what was then known about the actual facts of female sex anatomy and physiology and entered the realm of speculation, he came, as we have seen, to serious grief. We have therefore, to forestall similar errors in our own thinking, taken considerable trouble to acquaint ourselves thoroughly with every aspect of this new research. In presenting it here in a simplified digest form, we hope to make this little known material, gathered from the literature and above all from personal interviews with the researchers themselves, available, both to the medical and behavioral science professions, as to the intelligent public at large. Besides, only with a clear understanding of the scientific principles involved in these aspects of the problem, can the rest of our discussion assume its correct importance.

Briefly and simply stated, the scientific investigations to which we are referring are concerned with the question: "What happens to the woman's body when it is sexually aroused?"

To answer this question, scientists have had to take large numbers of complicated physical, chemical, and electronic measurements on scores of women who volunteered to have their pulse-rate, heart beat, respiration, metabolism, vaginal acidity, brain waves, etc. measured during various stages in their sexual response cycle.

What kind of women would agree to submit to studies that seem to dehumanize and degrade to the level of animal physiology one of the most intensely human, personal, and intimate acts of which the individual is capable?

On first blush one would think that only the type of woman who is used to surrendering her body in the most impersonal manner possible, and who regards her sex primarily as an object of barter, namely the professional prostitute, would agree to this kind of experimentation. If this was indeed the case, one would want to know immediately the general validity of the results obtained with such atypical human subjects.

In the beginning we learned that this research into the female sex response was indeed carried out with prostitutes and their male associates. Leaving aside for the moment the moral and human side of the problem, this factor alone would perhaps not have been a serious drawback from the scientific point of view. After all, it was not the psychology, but the anatomy and physiology of the woman's sex response which were to be studied. And there was little reason to believe that the body of the woman who puts a cash value on her professional sex contacts would react differently from the body of any other woman.

It came, therefore, as a surprise and a disappointment to the scientific investigators when they discovered that they could *not* use professional prostitutes for their experiments. This was because it transpired that the sex organs of the active professional prostitute tended to be more or less constantly in a state of mild congestion. The reason for this is that active prostitutes are exposed to a great deal of physical sex stimulation which is not followed by complete physical tension-release during orgasm. Their *physiological* state is, therefore, similar to that of the young and inexperienced bride on her honeymoon, who is subject to a great deal of physical and psychological sex stimulation, but who has not yet experienced orgasmic tension-release in her sexual relations. In other words, the physiological state of the professional prostitute does not provide a reliable point of departure from which to measure the manifestations of sexual arousal during various stages of the woman's response-cycle.

As the scientists were forced to search for other female subjects, they found that it was not as difficult as they might have thought to find perfectly respectable volunteers, such as nurses, secretaries, housewives, and even some women from the higher-income professions. It was, naturally, to be expected that the women who volunteered for these experiments would constitute a group of different psychological make-up from other women in the general population. But any subtle factors in their psychology could not seriously affect the physiological and anatomical measurements that were at issue.

Also, it turned out that one technological device was particularly helpful in studying the physical manifestations of the woman's sex response: the *motion picture camera*. If the woman whose physical sex responses were under observation was allowed to provide auto-erotically for the necessary stimulation, the camera, with the use of color film, was able to record the outward or surface phenomena, such as skin discoloration, changes in breast-size, etc. But in addition, by opening the vaginal canal with the use of a speculum, it was also possible accurately to observe and make a permanent record of the *internal* changes which take place under sexual stimulation.

The advantage of this technique lay in the fact that a study could be made of the subtle and rapid physiological and anatomical reactions which manifest themselves during the various phases of the woman's total sex response by slowing down the film. By the use of this technique, the scientist is obviously able to make his observations any number of times, without the need for additional experiments.

These film records of women's sex responses constitute a most valuable adjunct to all the other measurements which were taken from a group of over one hundred women in the particular research setting to which we refer. The results thus obtained are therefore to be regarded as highly reliable. In our opinion, they are not only to be taken seriously, but to be used as the background for any meaningful future discussion of female sexuality.

We are now ready to examine what modern science has to tell us about the physical side of woman's sex response.

It appears that woman's total sex response follows a *cyclical pattern* which can be divided into four phases which scientists refer to as 1) *excitement*, 2) *plateau*, 3) *orgasm*, and 4) *resolution*.

These descriptive terms are used to include numerous physiological changes which flow progressively from one stage to the next, if the woman is sufficiently stimulated to the point of orgasm. We must, however, remember that many of these physical reactions are so fleeting that they are difficult to notice by ordinary methods of observation.

EXCITEMENT PHASE

A woman can enter into the first, or *excitement phase* of her total sexual response cycle in one of two ways, or a combination of both: by *physical* stimulation, such as kissing, fondling, etc.; or by *psychological* means, such as reading or viewing erotically stimulating material, being in the presence of others in whom she has an erotic interest, or by simply thinking and day-dreaming about something which has an erotic significance to her.

How can one tell when a woman has entered into the excitement phase?

Vagina

Research shows that ten to thirty seconds of such physical or mental stimulation are sufficient to produce the first sign of a woman's sexual response: *vaginal lubrication.*

It stands to reason that a woman's excitement phase may vary in length from a few minutes to a matter of several hours, depending on the situation and the nature of the stimulation. The scientists measure this phase from the onset of any form of sexual stimulation, until the woman enters her second or *plateau* phase of response. However, as one may also expect, this stage, together with the last or *resolution* phase, takes up most of the time consumed in the woman's total sexual response cycle.

Bartholin Glands

One of the scientific surprises relevant to the *excitement* phase was, the researchers informed us, that the vaginal lubrication is *not* produced by the Bartholin glands, as was formerly assumed.

All that the Bartholin glands contribute is a mere drop or two of mucoidal material which appears only after prolonged stimulation *after* the vagina has already been well lubricated.

If the vagina is opened for examination during the excitement phase, it can be observed that separate little drops of lubrication appear scattered over the entire vaginal wall. These drops look like the beads of perspiration that form on an individual's forehead, and this phenomenon has therefore been called the "sweating" reaction of the vagina.

As sexual tension mounts, these droplets will come together to form a smooth, glistening coating on the vaginal wall. This vaginal lubrication continues, though at a greatly reduced rate, throughout the woman's response cycle as long as sexual stimulation is carried on. It only stops completely after orgasm has been achieved.

At the same time as this "sweating" reaction of the vagina there occur several other changes of the woman's internal sex organs: the inner two-thirds of the vaginal walls balloon out to increase from two to three times their normal width. As this expansion takes place, the normally washboard-like surface texture of the vaginal walls flattens out, producing a smooth surface, and the entire vagina becomes noticeably darker in color. Meanwhile, the vagina is lengthened from two to four centimeters, depending on the woman's previous childbearing experience. This increase in the vagina is essentially accomplished before the *plateau* phase is reached.

In order to understand the expansibility of the vagina during the excitement phase, the scientists explained, we must bear in mind that "anatomically the vagina is a *potential*, rather than an actual space." Unless the woman is menstruating, or some degree of sexual tension exists, the front and the back walls of the vagina lie about as closely together, "as the sides of a folded piece of paper." Despite this collapsed state of the unstimulated vagina, the experts tell us, the normal vagina is capable of expanding to an almost unlimited extent.

Cervix

Simultaneously with the vagina's expansion, the cervix is pulled back and away from the opening of the vagina. This, we are given to understand, is "part of a total uterine movement" by which the uterus is pulled upward into the "false pelvis." Neither the nature of this anatomical movement, nor its possible purpose, we were told, are as yet fully understood.

These internal changes during the excitement phase are also accompanied by certain changes in the *external* genitalia.

Clitoris

The clitoris, a highly sensitive organ with a tremendous blood circulation for its size, becomes enlarged as the woman is being sexually stimulated. This increase, the researchers explain, may be very small, but in some women it can amount to two or three times its normal size.

Labia Majora

Other changes which occur in the external female sex organs during the excitement phase concern the labia majora and minora. For the woman who has not had children, the labia majora or large labia thin out and flatten upward and backward against the pelvis, increasing somewhat in size as they do so. For the woman with multiple birth experience, the labia majora may increase in size from two to three times. But even such distended labia tend to spread sideways toward the end of the excitement phase, making the vaginal opening more accessible for sexual intercourse.

Labia Minora

The changes in the labia minora are more easily observable and are even more marked than those of the labia majora. In fact, so dramatic is the nature of this response, especially with regard to the color changes which take place, that it has been given a special name and called the "sex-skin" re-action of the woman. In its intensity it can justly be com-pared to the changes which take place in the labia of the monkey bitch whose entire vulval area discolors to a dull red when the animal is in heat and ready to receive the male.

In the human, the labia minora turn *bright pink* in color during the excitement phase and, as sexual tension increases, they swell up to about twice their normal size. Besides in-creasing in normal thickness, the labia minora (like the labia majora) extend sideways, thus re-enforcing the strength of the vaginal walls. As this takes place, the vagina may gain a whole centimeter or centimeter and a half in length during coitus.

Breasts

The only other changes which take place during the ex-citement phase concern the reactions of the breasts. These changes are more easily observable and had already been known to a certain extent prior to the research on which we are reporting. The latest findings have, therefore, added mainly to our knowledge of the precise *extent* to which these reactions take place rather than discovering their existence.

The most widely recognized response of the breasts to sexual stimulation is the well-known erection of the nipples. This erection reaction occurs in both breasts as the result of contraction of the muscular fibers within the nipples; but they do not always achieve full erection simultaneously. One nipple may become erect rapidly while the other lags behind the first, both in erection-time and size. Research shows that the nipples may increase in length from 1.0 to 1.5 cm., and in diameter at the nipple base from 0.5 to 1 cm. beyond their normal size.

A woman's nipples may, of course, become erect without any sexual stimulus. For instance, when exposed to cold, or when a tight undergarment is suddenly removed, or if the woman has been resting on her stomach.

Naturally, the original size of the woman's nipples will make a difference with regard to their potential increase in length and diameter. This does *not* mean that large, protruding nipples have more capacity for expansion than average-sized nipples. However, under stimulation, small nipples show only a slight increase in length and little, if any, increase in diameter at the base.

A special situation exists if the woman has inverted nipples. In that event, they may reverse themselves under sexual stimulation to a semi-erect position, but in other cases may show no outward signs at all.

Another anatomical response in the woman's breasts which is so conspicious that it is easily recognized consists in the veins of the breast surfaces becoming engorged. These bluish markings are most clearly visible on larger breasts, but may be noticed first over the front of the chest, before appearing on the breasts themselves.

To most people it will not be surprising to hear that there is an enlargement of the whole breast under sexual stimulation. Less known is the fact that this enlargement may amount to an increase of up to one-fifth or one-quarter over the woman's normal breast size.

Still another sign of the woman's sexual arousal which has been recognized more frequently is the fact that the colored areas surrounding the nipples (areolae) begin to become quite visibly enlarged during the final stages of the excitement phase.

PLATEAU PHASE

If there is continued, effective stimulation, the woman goes from the excitement phase into the second or *plateau* phase of the sexual response cycle. At this level, the researchers have found, the woman's body "undergoes marked physiological strain" as the woman reaches a state of complete arousal (tumescence) of breasts, perineum, and vagina. This is the stage at which the woman frequently ceases to pay attention to minor irrelevant outside stimuli, such as noises from the environment which would normally disturb her sex response at the earlier stages of sexual arousal.

The plateau phase, we are told, is generally of much shorter duration than the preceding excitement phase. However, the plateau phase may be regarded as "the base line from which the woman climbs with relative ease and rapidity to orgasm." It is also the level to which she returns after experiencing a successful orgasmic experience. As one report puts it, "the woman gathers in the plateau phase physiological and psychological strength from the stockpile of mounting sexual tension." Having succeeded in this, she can now direct all her physical and mental forces toward a "leap into orgasm" during the third and most important phase of her total sexual response cycle.

At this stage it is absolutely vital that effective sexual stimulation is continued until the woman reaches orgasm. If this is not the case and stimulation is suddenly withdrawn, "the woman will drop slowly from the plateau phase into a prolonged and frustrating *resolution* phase."

Research has shown that during the plateau phase several further important physical changes occur which are necessary if the woman is to arrive at orgasmic tension-release.

Vagina

As already indicated, the "sweating" or lubricating reaction of the vagina continues at a reduced rate through this part of the woman's response cycle. This lubrication results in a change of the vagina's acidity ratio (pH), meaning that the vaginal environment becomes more favorable for the male sperm.

Continued also is the engorgement of the outer third of the vagina which had started to develop during the previous excitement phase. Now the vaginal canal becomes still more engorged and constricted as more and more blood is trapped in the woman's interior and exterior sex organs.

Breasts

The breasts show several changes, some of which are continued from the previous excitement phase. The colored areas of the breasts surrounding the nipples become quite puffy. Actually, the colored areas can become so swollen at this time that the erect nipples are partially hidden, and one can get the erroneous impression that their initial erection has been lost.

The breasts themselves reach the extremes of their enlargement in this phase which may, as we have seen, be considerable. This increase in breast size is more marked in the virginal breast which has not been used for nursing than in the pendulous or slack breast. This is particularly true, the researchers point out, for the woman who has either nursed without effective breast support or has experienced considerable breast engorgement following delivery.

During the plateau phase, the breasts may show yet another, and very dramatic response. There is a *measle-like rash* which may make its appearance as the woman rises from excitement to the plateau phase. This rash consists of a *pink mottling* which frequently appears over the front, side and ultimately the lower surfaces of the breasts. Actually, it first appears over the upper abdomen and spreads to the breast surfaces during the later stages of the plateau phase. Ultimately, the skin-flush may extend to the arms, face, back, buttocks and thighs as severe tension develops in ultimate preparation for the orgasm. It is at this time that the flush actually coalesces, "resembling an advanced state of measles."

The intensity of this reaction varies among women, but it was found that "for certain individuals, the flush reaction is a direct indication of the degree of sexual stimulation achieved." The researchers, however, caution the over-zealous amateur investigator that this skin reaction is usually more noticeable in the blonde or redheaded woman than in the brunette, and that its absence even in a blonde or redhead is not itself an indication that she has not reached a similar stage of sexual tension as the woman in whom this phenomenon does occur.

Labia Minora

As we have seen, most of the changes in the cervix, uterus, clitoris, and labia majora take place, or at least get well under way during the first or excitement phase.

Research has, however, shown that the labia minora undergo a second highly dramatic color change during the plateau phase. During that stage, the labia minora or "sex-skin" which had taken on a bright pink color during the previous excitement phase, now turn a deeper *scarlet red* hue. But again, we are told, this color change of the "sex-skin" differs from one woman to another, depending in particular on the number of times she has given birth. In general, the labia minora of the woman who has not had children, may turn a *cardinal red*, while the labia of the woman who has given birth more than once, may instead turn almost a *burgundy red*.

In spite of these individual variations, the researchers emphasize, one can take the color-change in the woman's labia minora as, "the most reliable indicator of the degree of sexual tension which she may have achieved." More than that, scientific evidence indicates that if the labia minora have changed from the bright-pink of the excitement phase to the brilliant (primiparous) scarlet-red, or the (multiparous) burgundy color, "one may be sure that the woman has reached a satisfactory plateau phase." If that is the case, and "effective stimulation is continued" the scientists categorically declare, *"an orgasm is not only imminent, but is sure to occur!"* It usually takes no more, they add, than sixty to ninety seconds from the beginning of these color changes to the actual onset of the orgasm.

By the time all this takes place, we are told, the labia minora have increased at least *twice their normal size*, "thus adding a full centimeter or so to the functional length of the vagina." This lengthening of the labia minora is of no small importance in that it helps (together with the outer third of the vagina) in providing a "supportive platform which aids the vagina in its involuntary attempt to grasp the shaft of the penis."

The engorgement of the labia minora also serves to make the opening of the vagina more available for the insertion of the penis, but it is usually less obvious in the woman who has not borne children than in the woman who has given birth once or more.

Orgasmic Phase

As to the question of what *orgasm* actually consists of, the scientists stress the *uniqueness* of the experience. They state that "orgasm with its short duration and dynamic tension release is a *major sensory experience of a very unique nature*." By this they seem to mean that as a physiological and anatomical phenomenon it is clearly definable, identifiable, and measurable. They describe it as a *short, violent explosion* which may temporarily block out all other stimuli and which is *followed by quick tension release*.

Research indicates that the intensity of the orgasm is in direct proportion to the intensity of the physical reactions which the woman's body has undergone during the preceding excitement and plateau phases. Depending on these factors, "the actual orgasmic phase may last *from three to eight or even ten seconds*."

With regard to what happens to the various organs of the woman during the orgasmic phase, the scientists speak first of all about a "generalized response" to orgasm. This they describe as a pattern of local anatomical responses, acting more or less in unison and consisting of an involuntary contraction of the entire perineal body, the outer third of the vagina, the rectum, and the lower abdomen.

In addition, there is a "general pelvic reaction," and many other muscle groupings throughout the whole body may become involved. Among these reactions, the researchers list as some of the more common and easily noticeable ones the well-known stiffening of the neck muscles, the spastic contractions of the musculature of the hands, arms, feet, and legs, the swollen flushed face, and the expanded rib cage.

Scientists also call attention to the strained, flushed features of the woman approaching and during orgasm, "resembling those of an athlete at the peak of his performance, or of a person at hard labor, or even of an individual who is being tortured." At this point the woman may be so absorbed in her orgasmic experience that she no longer responds even to relatively strong stimuli of the environment.

Of course, the degree to which the woman's sex organs and her whole body may become involved in these physical manifestations depends entirely on the extent to which she has been sexually aroused, in other words on the intensity of the orgasm.

Vagina

During orgasm the woman's *internal* sex organs also show several very specific reactions. We recall that the outer third of the vagina becomes congested during the plateau phase. Now, during orgasm, this part of the vagina contracts in a definite rhythm, in a manner similar to the contractions of the penis at the moment of ejaculation.

A woman may have, we were told, from four to ten such rhythmic vaginal contractions during orgasm, with approximately one-eighth to one-tenth of a second between them.

Whether these vaginal contractions are noticeable by the man during intercourse depends again on a number of factors, the scientists hasten to point out. In the first place, the rhythmic vaginal contractions differ in intensity "from very slight tremorlike movements to strong, well-marked spasms." Obviously, if the contractions are very slight, they may not be easily noticeable. Or, during sexual intercourse, the man may be so absorbed in his own sex response, especially just prior to and during ejaculation, that he may be unable to perceive the vaginal contractions, even if they are relatively strong. What is more often felt by the man during coitus as a "gripping or tightening about the shaft of the penis," we were told, is actually the "constriction of the central portion of the vagina" which occurs as the woman approaches orgasm.

Another problem connected with the female orgasm which has been hotly debated by experts and would-be experts alike concerns the question: "Does the woman *ejaculate* during orgasm in some manner comparable to the ejaculation of the man?"

To this question, the researchers reply with an unequivocal *No!* They are quick to point out that the prostate gland and the seminal vesicles which contribute most of the man's ejaculatory fluid are only unimportant, poorly developed vestigial structures in the woman.

True, the musculatory contractions of the vagina during orgasm squeeze out some of the genital secretions. In a few exceptional cases, the genital secretions may even be ejected with some force. But, strictly speaking, one cannot use the term "ejaculation" for this kind of occurrence. In fact, the scientists informed us to our own surprise that it was precisely this phenomenon, or rather its *absence*, which constitutes the most outstanding feature which differentiates between the male and the female orgasm.

Cervix

In the past, it was thought that during orgasm the cervix ejected a mucous fluid (*crystella*) which was regarded as roughly the equivalent to the man's ejaculate. The most recent research has completely discredited this theory by demonstrating that the cervical entrance to the womb *remains absolutely dry* during the entire sexual act.

Scientists point to certain changes which take place in the cervix and uterus during orgasm. The reader will recall that during the excitement phase, the cervix is pulled back and upward as "part of a total uterine movement whose nature is not yet fully understood." Now, immediately after the orgasm, the small opening at the head of the cervix, leading into the uterus, becomes dilated. This cervical reaction, we are told, lasts through the first five to ten minutes of the next, or *resolution* phase before returning to normal.

At this point we asked the researchers the obvious question whether this slight dilation of the entrance to the womb is of any aid to the passage of the sperm. We were given to understand that if the dilation of the cervix had any such function, it would be of a purely passive nature. At any rate, the scientists are emphatic in their assertion that, "there is no active anatomic reaction with orgasm, such as a sucking effect" at the entrance to the womb which could possibly propel semen through the cervix into the uterus.

Uterus

This does not mean that there are no contractions of the uterus. To the contrary, it was found that, in addition to the vaginal contractions, the uterine walls do also contract rhythmically during orgasm. But the scientists stress the fact that the uterine contractions do not result in any sucking effect as was formerly thought to be the case.

The uterine contractions can be easily felt on the abdominal wall of the pregnant woman. The researchers even speculate that these contractions may be the real cause for the tendency of some women to lose a pregnancy, particularly during the first three months after conception. However, there is no indication that the average, healthy woman should refrain from sexual intercourse during pregnancy. Only those women with a tendency toward spontaneous abortion may be adversely affected by the uterine contractions during orgasm.

Rectum

We were told that it is possible for a woman to experience rectal contractions during orgasm. This reaction does not always occur, but when it does take place, it is an indication that the woman is experiencing a relatively *intense* orgasm. In other words, as the researchers put it, "during the more violent five- to ten-second type of orgasm," the woman's vaginal contractions are likely to be paralleled by "simultaneous spastic contractions of the perineal body and the external rectal sphincter."

More difficult to understand is the reaction of the perineum to orgasm. The scientists explain that this reaction consists in the main of a "spasmodic tightening of the perineal body" during the end of the plateau phase as the woman comes closer to experiencing orgasm. Then, during orgasm itself, "there may be an involuntary, irregular elevation of the entire perineum." However, this phenomenon may no longer occur in the woman with repeated birth experience.

Urethra and Urinary Bladder

We made special inquiries with regard to the frequently made assertion that the woman has a tendency to void urine during orgasm. The scientists assured us that this is a very infrequent phenomenon during *any* phase of the sexual response cycle. There is, the researchers point out, an occasional, involuntary spreading of the external urinary opening during orgasm. However, this dilation of the urinary opening is very minimal, does not occur with any kind of regularity, does not seem to be related to the intensity of orgasm, and does not necessarily cause involuntary loss of urine. On the other hand, the specialists admit, some women do report an urge to void during intercourse, particularly those who have not experienced childbirth and who have therefore a "higher and firmer perineum and a smaller vaginal outlet" than women who have had childbearing experience.

Multiple Orgasm

In still another attempt at clarification of a highly controversial point, we made specific inquiries on the matter of multiple orgasm. We were assured that the research data leave no doubt that woman has the capacity for genuine multiple orgasm, provided stimulation is continued during or shortly following the first orgasmic experience. If that is the case, the woman may return to the plateau phase and go from there to one or more subsequent orgasms in the same manner as before.

RESOLUTION

It is commonly assumed that it takes the woman longer to recover from an orgasmic experience than it takes the man. We found out that this is a mistaken notion, or at best a gross oversimplification of the matter. The research results indicate instead that the resolution phase which follows orgasm and which is the last phase in the woman's total response cycle, is "roughly proportional in its duration to that of the excitement phase."

In other words, the resolution will be very short, if the woman has experienced only a short excitement phase which is rapidly followed by plateau and orgasm. If, on the other hand, there has been a long drawn-out excitement phase, followed only by plateau, but without orgasmic tension release, the unrelieved sexual tension will cause an equally protracted and, as already pointed out, frustrating resolution phase. In that case, we are given to understand "the woman's sex responding organs will only gradually return to their normal state, even long after all sexual stimulation has ceased."

There were several other phenomena which the researchers explained to us as occurring during the resolution phase, some of which could have been expected, and others which were, frankly, to us, surprising.

Not so surprising may be the fact that the first and most easily recognizable sign of resolution after orgasm is the "appearance of a filmy perspiration" which spreads over the back, thighs, and chest. At the same time, the woman begins again to pay attention to and take a renewed conscious interest in her surroundings.

Frequently, there may be heavy perspiration from the armpits. Some women, we were told, "whose faces have been mottled in the usual patchy manner by the flush reaction" as orgasm approached, may also perspire noticeably on the forehead and upper lip. Other women have described to the researchers a sensation of either being excessively warm or, the opposite, of feeling cold and sweaty after an orgasm.

The studies have shown that simultaneously with the appearance of the filmy sweating reaction, the measle-like flush begins to disappear, first from the back, buttocks, the lower abdomen, arms, and thighs, then from the breasts, and finally from its primary source in the region of the stomach.

Clitoris

It may be more surprising that the generalized sweating reaction constitutes the first noticeable sign of resolution after orgasm and not, as one might have assumed, loss of clitoris erection. However, we were told that the clitoris is frequently the *last* of the woman's sex organs to return to normal size. This is, of course, especially true if the woman did not experience orgasm, thus remaining in a relative degree of sexual tension.

Vagina

The first sign of detumescence in the woman, comparable to loss of penis erection in the man, would be the rapid shrinking back of the engorged outer third of the vagina to its normal size. But rapid as this may be, it is still not as quickly completed as the parallel phenomenon in the penis.

After that, the expansion of the vagina in depth and width which took place during the excitement phase, slowly recedes. This process may take five to eight minutes until the vagina has returned to its normal state.

Needless to say, there has been no more lubrication from the time of orgasm. Nevertheless, it was found that the lubricating material may stay on the vaginal walls for an hour or two after the end of all sexual activity.

Breasts

We were told that during resolution the breasts slowly return to their normal size in a direct reversal of the way they developed during the excitement phase:

1) The measle-like skin rash disappears.
2) The enlarged breast returns to normal size.
3) The colored areas around the nipples (areolae) begin to lose their engorged, swollen appearance.
4) The nipples which have been partially hidden by the swollen area (areolae) surrounding them, reappear which can give one the false impression that the nipples are beginning to erect again.
5) The engorged surface veins return to their normal state.

The breasts frequently retain some degree of enlargement for a period of from five to ten minutes after orgasm. The rest of the symptoms of sexual tension which the breasts show during the excitement, plateau, and orgasmic phases disappear much more slowly. "One of the last signs of sexual excitement to disappear is the engorged condition of the surface veins," the researchers say. Frequently, the nipples have already returned to their normal size before the surface veins also take on their normal appearance.

Labia Majora

After orgasm, the labia majora return to their normal size and anatomical position. This process takes less time, the measurements show, in the woman without childbearing experience than in the woman who has borne children and whose labia are therefore likely to be more engorged.

Labia Minora

The labia minora likewise undergo changes during resolution in a sequence which is the reverse of that during the excitement phase. First they lose the discoloration, then they return slowly to their normal position and size.

The researchers point out that it generally takes no more than 90 to 120 seconds after the orgasm, before the labia minora lose their brilliant red or burgundy color and return to the light pink of the early excitement phase. After that, the change from the excitement phase pink to their normal brownish color is also relatively rapid, but progresses unevenly, resulting in a blotchy appearance. All in all, the total time which the labia minora require to return completely to their normal color is said to be about five minutes from the time of orgasm.

Cervix and Uterus

The researchers informed us that after orgasm, the cervix drops back into its normal position. This is also the case with the uterus, "as the vaginal walls collapse" during the resolution phase.

If anything is clear from all the accumulated data on the female sex response, it is that with regard to orgasm as a physiological and anatomical phenomenon (and we may add, still more so as a subjective psychological experience), one woman differs from another, and even within the same woman one finds much variation from one time to another.

This difference in the woman's response applies not only to the orgasm itself, but to the *pattern* of her entire response cycle, from the first indications of mounting sexual tension to the end of the resolution phase. In answer to our inquiries to that effect, we were given to understand that one common response pattern consists, for example, of a long excitement phase with periods of planned delay which is accomplished by slowing down the sexual stimulation. During this kind of "teasing" technique, the woman's sexual excitement will slowly mount and, if in this situation stimulation is suddenly reapplied, there may be a quick, explosive jump to orgasm, with little or no intermediate plateau phase. After such an intense experience of tension release, there frequently is an equally rapid resolution phase, "possibly even ending in deep sleep within sixty to ninety seconds after the orgasm."

Another response pattern—and one which is very regrettably and all too frequently found in our culture—is the one in which "the woman rapidly and smoothly advances through excitement to the plateau phase," only to get "stuck" and remain there in utter frustration, without being able to reach orgasm. In such cases, when there is no sex tension release through orgasm, the researchers point out, "the woman may remain in this state of animated, but frustrating sexual tension for hours, especially if some form of psychic sexual stimulation continues to exist." Technically, this would mean that in these cases the resolution phase takes an inappropriately long time, because there has been no dynamic tension release through orgasm. Under these circumstances, we were told, the return of the breasts and labia to their normal state may take *up to twelve hours*!

If one looks clearly and soberly at the impressive clinical data which have only recently been accumulated and which we have tried to present in the foregoing discussion, one emerges with two basic impressions: 1) the realities of woman's total sex response as they are known today are considerably different from previous conceptions of it, and 2) woman's orgastic capacity is at least equal to, if not greater than that of the man's, providing effective stimulation is available and the woman is in an emotional state to respond positively to such stimulation.

In the following chapters we shall try to demonstrate how *social attitudes* may affect woman's orgastic potential either favorably or unfavorably, and what personal and emotional factors enter into the picture to determine the orgastic capacity of the individual woman.

IV

The Sociology of Orgasm

WE have, in the preceding chapter, followed the truly startling discoveries in the anatomy and physiology of the female sex response. They have presented us with concrete evidence that there is no such thing as a vaginal, clitoral, or any other special kind of orgasm, but only a *difference in degree of intensity* that an orgasmic experience may assume. The same biological research also furnishes proof that many formerly held medical theories as well as popular opinions about the nature of woman's sex response have been erroneous.

We shall now consider some of the no less astonishing and revolutionary discoveries concerning female sexuality which have been contributed by the *social* sciences. They complement, as we shall see, the physical data, rendering them more meaningful, and shed light on those aspects of woman's sex response which would otherwise remain unexplainable.

Even some time before the natural scientists got seriously interested in the subject, cultural anthropologists like Margaret Mead had found that whether a woman is going to experience orgasm or not in her sexual relations depends not only on physical factors, but even more on—where she happens to have been born and brought up! In other words, whether the woman will ever experience the kind of physical and mental stimulation that is most likely to lead to orgasm depends to a large extent on the accident of birth and the culture in which she has been raised.

If, for example, the woman happens to be raised among one kind of people, say among the Mundugumur, a South Sea island group of fishing people, she is likely to have no trouble achieving orgasm in her sexual relations. If, on the other hand, she has had the bad fortune of having grown up among the Arapesh, another primitive tribe, her chances of ever experiencing orgasm would be very slim.

How do anthropologists explain this strange fact?

Margaret Mead informs us that the ability to achieve orgasm is a "*potential* that may or may not be developed by a given culture." In other words, a people like the Mundugumur believe in orgasm for the woman, while the Arapesh do not. The result is that Mundugumur women are generally orgastic and Arapesh women are likely to be anorgastic.

As Dr. Mead explains, in her opinion the female orgasm does not rest on the same simple *reflex* basis as the male orgasm, but involves a number of *learned responses*. It is these learned responses, according to this theory, that a given culture may either develop in its women or neglect.

But this explanation, in turn, becomes wholly satisfactory only if we combine it with what the biological experts now tell us about the physical aspects of the female sex response. If we listen to them, and their arguments are extremely convincing, virtually *any* woman can be brought to orgasm, providing *effective stimulation* is applied.

Professor Mead had said almost that much herself when calling attention to the fact that men in Samoan or French society do not expect their women to achieve orgasm by mere copulation. Men in these societies understand that most women do require some kind of clitoral stimulation, and are prepared to provide it in one form or another.

According to Margaret Mead:

> Both in France and in Samoa, happy sex relationships are postulated on the male's taking pride and pleasure in gratifying the female, in inducing in her a climax behavior comparable to his own. In neither Samoa nor France is simple copulation expected to produce such results.

If one now reinterprets Professor Mead's own anthropological findings in the light of the recent discoveries on the physiology and anatomy of the female sex response, one arrives at the following conclusion: clearly those societies which believe in orgasms for women and produce orgastic behavior in them *are also the ones which employ effective stimulation techniques*, whereas other societies apparently lack this kind of sexual sophistication.

Put differently, we suggest that if you took, say, an Arapesh woman who has never experienced orgasm with the stimulation techniques which are popular in that society and exposed her to a situation in which more effective stimulation techniques were employed, our hypothetical Arapesh lady would pass through a normal sequence of excitement, plateau, orgasmic, and resolution phases just like any Eskimo, Indian, American, British, or French woman under similar conditions.

But what happens to those sexually underprivileged women, like the Arapesh, to whom society does not give a chance to have a happy (orgastic) sex life? Are they regretful but resigned to their fate? Are they indifferent to their situation, not knowing what they are missing? Or are they openly discontented and rebellious?

Margaret Mead says that on the whole, Arapesh women don't seem to mind. Some of them, however, are keenly and painfully aware of their frustration and seek active means of satisfying their erotic needs. In Arapesh society, these sexually dissatisfied wives are definitely the *misfits*. They can be compared to those women of the Victorian era who dared to show any sexual feeling at all, or to that increasing minority of modern women who—like some of those whom we interviewed and whose sex life we shall subsequently discuss—are going beyond contemporary community standards in the expression of their erotic interests.

During the past century, one can say, Western society's mentality was, with respect to its attitude toward female sexuality, pretty much the same as that of the contemporary Arapesh. Very few people in England and America really cared at that time whether women achieved orgasm or not—including, apparently, the women themselves. In fact, at that time in England, America, and in many other European countries, an orgastic woman was considered somewhat of a freak of nature and regarded as a lewd and immoral person.

Of course, things have changed a lot since then in our culture. Ever since Freud started analyzing his first hysterical women patients in the early 1900's, the idea has gradually penetrated Western society that too severe a repression of our sexual impulses breeds neurosis. And more and more people over the past fifty years have come to understand that sexual enjoyment and orgasmic tension release are as important for the well-being of the female as for the male of the human species.

As Maxine Davis writes in her book, *The Sexual Responsibility of Women:*

> . . . It is of paramount importance that she [the woman] does experience orgasm.

It is hardly worth belaboring the point that the experience of orgasm is essential to woman's sexual happiness. Most people in America and Europe today believe in it, and those who don't cannot be convinced by any amount of logical argument.

Still, much is left to be desired. The recent Kinsey studies have shown that only slightly more than one third of American women have orgasm in most of their marital coitus during the first year of marriage. For the married women this percentage increases slowly over the years, but even after twenty years of matrimony *less than half* of all married American women respond *occasionally* to orgasm.

As for England, we hear from British marriage counsellor Dr. Eustace Chesser:

> A *substantial majority* [of English women] felt that they could still make a success of marriage, even if they did not enjoy sexual intercourse; and that they would remain con-

tented even though [only] their husbands—though not themselves—enjoy intercourse.

Some women claim and are able to convince clinicians
that they are happy in their marriages and content with their
sexual lives, even though they never or only seldom experience orgasm. But should we be justified in taking their statements at face value? We do not think so. For it has been our
experience that, if questioned in greater detail, many frigid
women who claim to be content with their lot break down
and confess that they really want nothing more than to experience at least once the complete sexual fulfillment that they
have only heard or read about.

On the other hand, the same English women on whom Dr.
Chesser had reported, and who had claimed with such mis-
placed optimism that they could "make a go" of marriage,
without sexual satisfaction on their side, became more and
more dissatisfied over time:

> The women [says Dr. Chesser] who rarely or never reach
> orgasm appear to constitute quite a separate group, in which
> the proportion finding intercourse pleasant falls off sharply
> after the first months of marriage.

We can well understand why women who do not experience orgasm gradually lose interest in sexual relations and
come to find intercourse unpleasant: as we have seen, considerable physical and emotional tensions are set up in the
woman's mind and body in the build-up toward orgasm.
Such conditions, if repeated over months and years, cannot
help but cause both physical and mental damage. One should
not therefore be surprised to hear that failure to achieve
sexual happiness is likely to have an adverse effect on the
woman's total relationship with her partner and may lead to
the breakdown of their relationship.

This does not necessarily mean that such a couple would
themselves be aware of the sexual roots of their marital

troubles. Everyone knows how easily sexual dissatisfaction is transferred to something else. In many of these cases, the couple do not quarrel at all about their sex life, but may violently disagree on a variety of irrelevant matters.

Other couples are tacitly aware of the source of their difficulties but keep pretending that it does not exist. Some time ago, we were advising a middle-aged couple about their rather serious marital problems. They were on the brink of divorce. Each was accusing the other of any number of things, none of which seemed to be serious enough to break up a marriage. There was even something about the manner in which the two people spoke about these things that made us feel that they were not really serious about it themselves.

Once, after having listened again to the long list of more or less irrelevant complaints by husband and wife, the discussion and analysis of which seemed to lead nowhere, we asked in sheer desperation: "Why don't you tell us more about your sex life?"

The question seemed even to us rather beside the point, for neither the husband nor the wife had ever, in all their long tirades, complained for one moment about any sexual dissatisfaction.

It came, therefore, as a surprise to us when the husband burst out, "Now you are talking! Why didn't you ask that question before?" And, all their previous problems forgotten, both husband and wife flooded us for an hour or two thereafter with a stream of bitter complaints about the other's sexual inadequacies.

Had they been dishonest with us? We don't think so. Dishonest toward each other? Perhaps. Dishonest toward themselves? Definitely, yes.

Clinical and personal experiences have taught us that there is a converse to this kind of situation which completes the picture: while sexual dissatisfaction is frequently at the bottom of many marital problems which seem to have no relation to sex at all, many marital problems of a non-sexual nature can be solved with some advice, or will even right themselves of their own accord, provided the couple's sexual adjustment is basically good and satisfactory.

To phrase this differently: if a couple is getting along well in the bedroom, the chances are that they will also learn how to get along in the living room. But the best of daytime manners are not good enough to make up for nighttime frustration.

From his studies of English married couples, Dr. Chesser seems to have arrived at similar conclusions. He remarks drily:

> There seems to have been a widespread diminution of the love felt for their husbands since the early days of marriage by those women who rarely or never experience orgasm in intercourse.

Considered from all these viewpoints, one can hardly overstress the point that orgasm-ability does indeed matter, if the woman is to be sexually happy, if she is to avoid nervous and psychosomatic disturbance, and if her marriage is to be successful.

There is really nothing very new about these insights. Ancient Oriental marriage manuals stressed the importance of orgasm for women—and surprisingly enough *especially for women*. If women do not achieve sexual happiness in orgasm, these ancient manuals warn, one had better be prepared to find them rather ill-humored, sickly, quarrelsome, and inclined to make trouble. The manuals, therefore, could not do enough to exhort men to keep their womenfolk sexually happy, if they themselves wished to live happy, peaceful lives.

If Freud felt—with reference to woman's supposed need to transfer sexual feeling from the clitoris to the vagina—that "anatomy is destiny," as far as her sexuality is concerned, the modern anthropologist would say the *social environment* is even more so, to which one may add (in agreement with Freud) that the *accidents of individual development* are of no less importance than the other two factors.

Expressed in its simplest terms, the latest formula for woman's orgastic capacity would therefore read something like:

$$\text{anatomy} + \text{social milieu} + \text{individual psychology} = \text{orgasm capacity.}$$

If that is of little comfort to the individual woman in her personal problems with orgasm, the realization that it all basically adds up to the type of stimulation techniques used and the absence of emotional blocking against the mental and physical stimulation provided, may be more encouraging. For if one cannot easily alter the anatomical structure of one's body, or choose the social and family environment into which one is born, one can, fortunately, do something about one's mental attitudes (even if it may take time and help) and, above all, one can do something about one's methods of love-making.

V

Portrait of Four Women

THERE are four women who are the principal protagonists in the chapters which follow and whom we shall come to know intimately from their sex histories. We shall call them The More-Than-Average Housewife, The Married Lesbian, The Doctor's Wife, and The Sexual Sophisticate.

The More-Than-Average Housewife was basically "average" in all respects but one: the strength of her sex-drive and the alacrity with which she was willing to talk about it.

She was the sporty, outdoor type who saw herself more as a companion of her three pre-adolescent children than as an older authority figure. She loved a good time, enjoyed simple pleasures such as good food, good drink, and clothes. She was most partial to undemanding social life: an evening with friends, a little dancing now and then, a movie or two a month, an occasional dinner at a good restaurant, and, above all, plenty of good, wholesome sex, to paraphrase her own very direct manner of putting things. Of the four women, she was the most indigenously and typically *American*. Her type would have been unthinkable anywhere else.

The Married Lesbian seemed to us essentially Lesbian, not necessarily because she had had Lesbian experience, but because she exhibited the typical background and personality of a Lesbian woman. The fact that she was married and the mother of two young children could not alter her psychological predisposition toward members of her own sex, and continued to blight her efforts toward a satisfactory hetero-sexual adjustment.

She had the manners of the "upper set" and comported her-self in the style of a grande dame of the 1900's, and this was anything but put on or inappropriate for her. She did in fact come from one of those few upper-class American families who, by their international background and inherited wealth, continued to live in a style more appropriate to the require-ments of pre-1914 Europe than of contemporary American society.

By temperament she was an intellectual bohemian who was ill-suited to the management of a household and the normal upbringing of children. Nevertheless, she was doing both fairly well and was not seriously lacking in either function.

The Doctor's Wife was a strong, healthy human animal with animal appetites. She belonged to the sexy, Mediter-ranean type of female, epitomized by such stars of the Italian cinema as Sophia Loren or Anna Magnani. She was interested in politics, civic affairs, men in general, and her husband in particular, as well as in children and cats. She was a good and loving mother of her small brood, four in all. But her maternal instincts had been satisfied, and she wanted no additions to the family.

There was something slightly eccentric in the way she dressed, talked, and showed herself to the world. But she never went beyond the bounds of respectability and the socially acceptable, making it clear that she was always con-scious of the extent to which she intended to flirt with the bizarre and unconventional.

The Sexual Sophisticate was a rare type. There were many incongruities and conflicting characteristics in her make-up. Third generation American though she was, she had lived abroad long enough to confuse the lines of her national origin. Good looking and aware of it in an absent-minded sort of way, she resembled a displaced artist in her professional milieu rather than the social scientist she was.

Of lower middle-class background, upper educational level, indeterminate economic status, American nationality and international sympathies, she was impossible to place either in a class or a geographical point of origin.

Married, without children, she was living with her husband, to whom she was attached by strong bonds of affection, more like an intimate friend and lover in a kind of relationship which even the term "companionate marriage" could not satisfactorily describe.

Out of the several hundred female informants we interviewed, we focused, as we said earlier, on these four very differing types of women, because each exemplified certain aspects of female sexuality which had up to now been very little understood. In addition, we brought in another participant who contributed in other significant ways to our discussion, the Female Psychoanalyst. She was of European origin, the mother of two young adults and a sensitive, artistically inclined woman and capable therapist. We occasionally called on her for a professional opinion which differed quite often from our own and which represented the present trend of eclectically oriented psychoanalytic practice. With these introductions, we can proceed to a critical analysis of the sex-histories of our selected informants. We shall review their sexual experiences, personal feelings, and individual preferences in the light of the new clinical knowledge and sociological understanding presented in the previous discussion. In so doing we can simultaneously test the new scientific findings against the real-life material of our detailed case histories, as well as interpret these personal data by means of what is now known about the physical, sociological, and psychological aspects of the female sex response.

PART II

VI

The Struggle for Orgasm

Oᶠ the four women whose experiences form the basis of this discussion, three—the More-Than-Average Housewife, the Married Lesbian, and the Sexual Sophisticate have been especially concerned with their personal struggle for orgasm and what its attainment had meant to them.

Tʜᴇ Sᴇxᴜᴀʟ Sᴏᴘʜɪsᴛɪᴄᴀᴛᴇ

Beginning with our Sexual Sophisticate, we find that she did not reach orgasm easily. The experience of her first orgasm brought with it the sudden realization that she had unconsciously been longing for it when she was still too unsophisticated to think in terms of orgasm, or even of sexual intercourse itself:

> Like most young girls, I had always been vaguely longing for my Prince Charming to come and awaken me with his magic kiss. But when I had my first kiss and many more without the promised results, I was deeply disappointed. It was not until much later when, *after a deep and satisfying orgasm*, I suddenly realized the true meaning of the fairy tale and the nature of the magic kiss of which it speaks.

Did she experience a certain degree of satisfaction, before she became aware of orgasm? We specifically questioned our informant on this point, and received the following reply:

I can truthfully say that I did find sexual relations stimulating and pleasurable for some time before I experienced my first orgasm. I also gladly admit that if I did repeat the act over and over again without orgasm, I must have been deriving some kind of gratification from it. But to this I must add the postscript that I have at the same time always felt left in a high state of tension, dissatisfied, and slightly depressed.

There is no question in my mind that, if things had gone on in that fashion, I would soon have grown indifferent toward sex, or even have come to dislike it intensely, and possibly have given it up altogether in the long run.

The important thing in our Sexual Sophisticate's account seems to be that she felt her earlier sexual relations—even though they did not yet include orgasm—were nevertheless leading *somewhere*. She knew where she wanted to go, even though she did not always know how to get there. In this respect, every sexual experience became to her yet another stage on the road to orgasm and not just a cul-de-sac to further frustration. Had this not been so she would, according to her own emphatic statement, have abandoned hope and ultimately become disinterested or bitter about sex, as do many women after a number of similar experiences.

But to continue with our Sexual Sophisticate's own account of her problems in achieving orgasm and her ways of overcoming them:

I was not one of those rare or privileged women who achieved orgasm the first time they had sex. In fact, it was some time after I had begun sexual activities that I succeeded in having orgasm. Having once succeeded did not mean that from then on orgasm came easily for me every time I had sex. To the contrary, I found that after my first experience of orgasm, I was trying too hard to overcome my inhibitions and to achieve orgasm so that I frequently thwarted it by my own efforts.

At the time of my struggle for orgasm, I was in analysis. Still I am inclined to give my analysis less credit for my present degree of relative sexual freedom than other outside factors, though it certainly had a good deal to do with it. What, I believe, helped me the most was my husband's understanding attitude and our mutual feeling that sex was pleasurable and fun.

Outside of this, I would say, what proved helpful in liberating me, was that my husband and I informed ourselves as much as possible on sexual matters. By learning more about the facts of sex, we started to become a bit more objective, less emotional—a better word would perhaps be less hysterical about it. That in turn made us sufficiently free to experiment with a wider variety of techniques of love-making to bring more variety into our sex life.

Putting it simply and honestly, I have always learned best by doing.

As we have seen, our informant attributed her initial difficulty in achieving orgasm to her own excessive zeal. And we ourselves have found in our clinical practice that many women make exactly the same mistake. Instead of relaxing and abandoning themselves to the natural build-up of sexual tension, they distract themselves by their conscious efforts.

As to our informant's statement about "learning best by doing," we would like to compare it to a similar remark by Maxine Davis in her book, *The Sexual Responsibility of Women,* in which she emphasizes some degree of practical experience as necessary in sex, so that what the young girl might have read about it should become personally meaningful to her.

She writes:

A girl may have studied marriage manuals diligently and tried to absorb any instructions made available by objective, responsible people. But if she has never kissed or petted or masturbated or dreamed to the point of climax, she has not the faintest idea of what that supreme experience might be like.

As if to illustrate the point, the female English novelist, Joan Grant tells us in her autobiography *Time out of Mind* how she had taken the phrase "to sleep with someone," so literally that she thought she had actually become an "adulteress" when on one occasion she had merely shared the bed with her former fiancé.

In her naïveté and honesty she not only mistakenly convinced her scandalized parents that she had had sexual relations with that young man, but also some of her friends as well as her future husband to whom she had confessed this fact before their wedding. The young bridegroom was, therefore, quite astonished at the start of their honeymoon when he found her as much a virgin as anyone could be. The following discussion then ensued between the newlyweds:

"As a matter of interest, why did you tell me that you were an adulteress?"
I felt myself blushing. "Oh damn! I hoped you wouldn't notice. It makes me feel such a fool."
"Virgins are proverbially foolish."
"Not as foolish as I am! I never realized I had such an appallingly literal mind. I thought 'going to bed with a man' and 'sleeping with a man' meant just that."
"But you must have read books . . ."
"Books! Scientific books!" I exclaimed bitterly. "Words like fallopian tubes and spermatozoa—just *words*! I thought spermatozoa crept out and crept in while both parties were asleep. . . ."
He laughed until I was afraid that Malcolm or Betty would hear him.

Continuing with the history of our Sexual Sophisticate, we find her in the next statement emphasizing certain other psychological factors which played an important role in her personal struggle for orgasm:

At first, there were numerous and vague fears that haunted me. I wanted to get rid of them, but they were tenacious and persisted for a long time in spite of all my efforts to conquer them.
It is difficult to find word symbols that are adequate for the description of feelings such as these. Yet, I shall try.
Imagine you are in a jet plane, approaching the sound barrier. Now that you are about to hit the sound barrier, an

unspeakable fear suddenly seizes you: "What if at the moment that you break through, you might simply explode and disintegrate into so many fragments, as actually happened with some of the early experimental jets?"

Or imagine that you are under a general anaesthetic and about to lose consciousness. Just then the fear may grip you that your body is dissolving and that you are losing yourself into an oceanic nothingness from which there may be no return. . . .

However, if you succeed in overcoming these anxieties even once, the peace, quietude, relaxation, and satisfaction that are yours "on the other side" are so reassuring that it is that much easier to "let yourself go" the next time, and the next, and the next. . . .

We do not feel that the kind of orgasm anxiety to which our informant referred is in itself a sign of neurosis. After all, one must not forget that there is actually a physiological basis for this type of anxiety. For during what the medical researchers have called the plateau phase when sexual tension is very high, a mild state of anoxia (lack of oxygen in the brain tissue) begins to develop which is responsible for the typical clouding of consciousness at the moment of orgasm. It is undoubtedly for this reason that in the French language the experience of orgasm is commonly referred to as *la petite mort* (the little death) or *la mort douce* (the sweet death).

Further evidence comes from Japanese sociologist Miyataka Gaikotsu who made a study of the exclamations of women during orgasm. He proves that these exclamations nearly always refer to death, and therefore entitled his essay, *Jakumetsu-Iraku-Ko*, literally translated, *Investigation of Annihilation Experienced as Joy*.

Our Sexual Sophisticate gave us yet another personal insight which proved a new and important understanding of the kind of psychological problems which may complicate the woman's sex response. She told us that a woman may consciously want to linger in the plateau phase, and in so doing inadvertently short-circuit her own build-up to orgasm:

I have at times found my physical sensations before orgasm so pleasurable that I have hesitated to give them up and go on to orgasm. Because once you leave this pleasurable state, you cannot recapture the same exquisite pleasure which is yours at the time.

I realize that after the orgasm I can return to this state, and later have another orgasm or several orgasms, but it is never exactly the same. In that case, the sensations before orgasm may be either more pleasurable or less pleasurable than the first time, but they will definitely be *different*.

I think there is a delicate balance between rushing the orgasm, or delaying it too long. There have been times when I have dallied so long in this pleasant state that when I finally did have orgasm, it was only a weak and disappointing one.

What apparently happened to our informant at these occasions was that, instead of building up to an explosive sexual release, tension slowly dissipated itself during a too long drawn-out plateau phase.

In taking into account this particular problem which women may experience by consciously attempting to prolong the pleasurable pre-orgasmic phase one must avoid regarding it as an exclusively female problem. On the contrary, it seems analogous to the problems of men who during intercourse may dissipate the build-up of sexual tension by witholding orgasm too long. The difference between the male and female sex response does, on the other hand, apply with regard to the problem of multiple orgasm which our informant mentioned in this connection. With the human male there can hardly ever be the question of subtle nuances between a number of consecutive orgasms in the manner that our informant here speaks of them.

THE MORE-THAN-AVERAGE HOUSEWIFE

Coming to the More-Than-Average Housewife, we find that she had engaged in sexual relations for a considerably longer period than the Sexual Sophisticate before she began to experience orgasm with any degree of regularity.

As she did not give up her struggle for sexual happiness in spite of the many disappointing experiences which came her way, this can only be taken to indicate how keenly she felt the need for complete sexual fulfilment.

In her sex-history we find numerous references to this intense drive for orgasm. She actually gauged all her sexual relations with reference to this objective, telling us—in her own peculiar Henry Millerian style—how much closer she thought the one or the other of her experiences had brought her to the desired goal; so, for instance:

> As I was recovering from an operation during the war, I met a former boxer in the hospital. He was truly "built," sweet, but kind of dumb.
>
> We went to a hotel too soon after my operation, and it hurt at first. Later, it was the best yet.
>
> He undoubtedly had the longest penis I had ever seen. I know, I once had orgasm with him.
>
> However, I still didn't get on top; I wish I had. . . .
>
> Someone said the *size* doesn't matter, but it certainly seems to matter to *me*. The times I came nearest to orgasm were all with men who were rather well endowed. . . .
>
> Afterward I ran into another real good one on a bus. We warmed each other up during the ride by feeling and words, until we had to get off that bus and go to a hotel.
>
> We spent about five hours, doing it four or five times.
>
> Boy, he's another one I'd like to meet again! He was married and had five kids. But he told me this was the best yet for him. Too bad he had to report for duty somewhere, so that ended that.
>
> It seemed as if I was now meeting either better men, or I had improved. I think it was the former, because when I got to my husband, it wasn't as good as the last two, but pretty good.

If this passage is indicative of the strength of our informant's sex drive, the following example will show how much inconvenience she was willing to put up with in order to find sexual satisfaction.

> I remember, when my husband and I took a trip to visit his mother before we got married. We were about half way to our

destination and had been necking on the train. We just couldn't go any farther without making love, so we got off the train. We couldn't find a hotel room, as everything was taken within blocks of the station, since it was the end of the war.

Finally we found a room in an awful dump. We had to walk over some drunken bum lying in a passage to get to the bathroom. I was just about over menstruating which might account for the fact that I was so worked up. However, I just felt I had to get into that damn filthy bathroom, all the time asking myself if I figured it was worth it. It was. This makes me believe I have always gotten a mild orgasm, or sensation, but of course, it wasn't anything like I get now.

It is clear that our informant had received a certain amount of pleasure from her pre-marital relations with her husband (of the kind she had also received from several of her previous lovers) even though she did not experience full orgasm. Nevertheless, these experiences provided sufficient sexual pleasure for her to continue striving for an even more complete satisfaction. In fact, this woman's feeling that her fiancé would help her achieve complete orgasm weighed very heavily in her choice of this man as her future husband:

Even though I still didn't have a real bang-up, high-in-the-sky orgasm when we were not yet married, but going together, I could see he was capable of helping me get there, if anyone was.

Even after marriage, our More-Than-Average Housewife's troubles with achieving orgasm were by no means over,

The first year of our married sex life was good for my husband, I gather, and I guess for me too. However, I told him I still didn't think I was getting a whole orgasm.

The most important point in this statement is our informant's casual reference to the fact that she shared her difficulties in achieving orgasm with her husband, and in so doing actively engaged his assistance in overcoming them. Had she done otherwise and kept her troubles to herself, she would have deprived herself of this potential source of help. Still worse, if she had simulated orgasm, as many women foolishly do, she might well have entered into a life of continuous lies and pretences which could have undermined her marriage right from the start. For this honesty on her part, our More-Than-Average Housewife did not want to take any credit:

> I couldn't fake satisfaction, because I can't fake anything. I've tried . . . and he knows. He'll say, "It wasn't so good, eh?"

Superficially this statement does not appear very significant. But in fact it reveals the husband's positive attitude toward his wife's difficulties with orgasm. When the wife failed to be fully satisfied during intercourse, he did not make a big issue of it, nor did he start blaming her for her failure, as many men do. Neither did he take it personally and feel threatened in his masculinity by his wife's problem, as other less understanding men might have done.

Still, one may be sure that our More-Than-Average Housewife is speaking for many other women when she says:

> It's hard to be tired, to be bored with house, children, work and then suddenly switch off those worries and get into a romantic mood. It was easier as an unmarried, irresponsible, happy-go-lucky single girl. The desire is always there, but it takes a change of pace to stir it up.
>
> My husband is even worse off than I in this respect. He can't perform if he's mad, or if he has a hell of a big worry.
>
> I can still get interested in sex, even if I'm in a foul mood or worrying about something, if I just manage to switch my mind. But sometimes, I can't. For instance, if one of the kids is real sick, it's almost impossible to get your mind off that and onto sex.
>
> Thank goodness, my husband doesn't get mad often, or worry too much, and the kids don't get real sick often, otherwise, I'd be in one hell of a fix.

In this passage our informant helps to shatter the popular myth that women are more easily affected by worries or distracted during intercourse than men. She asserts just the opposite: it is her husband who finds it more difficult to take his mind off his worries, not she!

But apart from the occasional worries and upsets which could temporarily disturb her sex life, our informant felt that she had to contend with a serious *anatomical* handicap. The caprice of nature, she thought, happened to have burdened her with the fact that she either did not possess a clitoris at all, or that it was buried so deeply that it could not provide sufficient stimulation for her:

> My husband tells me that he doesn't think I have a clitoris, or that it is buried too deep, because he manually stimulated many a girl during the war who had orgasm that way. One was a married girl in England whose husband wasn't satisfying her, and she had at least one orgasm this way before he even entered her. Yet, he does that to me and I don't—damn my luck!
>
> Sometimes I wonder myself whether I have a clitoris. If I do, I can't understand why masturbation doesn't do anything for me, except excite me. But more likely it's just buried too deep, like my husband says. That might explain why I only have orgasm after so much friction and pressure in the mounted position.

We do not quite understand how this woman and her husband could have arrived at the very unlikely conclusion that she did not possess a clitoris. Obviously, she must have had one, if manual stimulation of that area could produce a positive sex response in her, even if it did not lead to orgasm.

There is, of course, always the remote possibility that the woman's clitoris may actually be completely buried in the surrounding tissue, as our informant also suspected. Simple medical inspection should have been able to disclose such a condition, if it actually existed, and once and for all settled the problem for that couple.

Our informant's worries about her clitoris also emphasize the over-concern of many people about the size of this organ. The truth is that *size* does not seem to matter at all in this respect. What does matter, on the other hand, is the relative *distance* of the clitoris from the vaginal outlet. Dickinson, for example, felt that if the base of the clitoris was located more than one-and-a-half inches above the vaginal outlet, its chances for receiving stimulation from the movement of the penis during intercourse were greatly reduced. Other investigators (for instance, Landis) have insisted that it was not the position of the clitoris which mattered, but its ability for *displacement.*

Common sense would indicate that there is much to recommend either of these two points of view. Obviously, if the clitoris is located too high above the vaginal outlet, it could probably not be effectively stimulated by most coital techniques. On the other hand, the general ability of the clitoris for displacement may work either for or against maximum stimulation, depending on the techniques employed. It may well be that in vaginal coitus the flexibility of the clitoris would make it more accessible to stimulation from the shaft of the penis. However, in manual stimulation of the clitoris, and even in mouth-genital contacts, the same ability of the clitoris for displacement can make it more difficult to apply consistent, effective stimulation to this small organ.

Another fascinating aspect of the female orgasm, and one which is rarely discussed, is the individual woman's *subjective experience* of it. Even the best of marriage manuals usually offer only the scantiest kinds of generalities on this point. For instance:

> The descriptions which women give of their sensations during the orgasm vary considerably. "A feeling of completion," "a tingling all over," "waves coming one after another in ever-widening circles," "balloons bursting inside"—these are some of the phrases women have used to describe an orgasm.

The obvious reason for the lack of more precise information on this subject is, of course, the fact that subjective experiences like these are extremely difficult to describe with any degree of accuracy. This is precisely why more general statements like, "my orgasm comes from the clitoris," or, "my orgasm comes from the vagina" which one frequently hears have so little validity.

THE SEXUAL SOPHISTICATE

With these reservations, we shall see what our informants had to say on this elusive matter. Starting with the Sexual Sophisticate, we find that her description of orgasm in spite of its poetic quality coincides rather well with the physical facts as they are known today:

> Sometimes I feel as if I'm climbing higher and higher and my vagina is getting tighter and tighter, or that the vagina is getting smaller and smaller until it can contract no further, but must explode into orgasm.
>
> At other times, I feel as if I'm sinking down and down toward some kind of bottom where the body tension feels to be concentrated, until it is gradually released by the quiet rhythmic contraction of the vagina.
>
> All I can think of in trying to compare the rhythm of this sensation, is the image of sea anemones, gently opening and closing, or the effortless breathing motions of a sleeping person.

THE MARRIED LESBIAN

We hesitated to ask our Married Lesbian how she experienced climax because she insisted that she had never had vaginal orgasm. Still, vaginal or not, she gave us a most convincing and beautiful description of orgasm:

> The first time I had an orgasm, it felt great. It's like a crescendo on a violin. Very unilinear, very simple, very chaste. Something going up to a peak and then dropping.

THE MORE-THAN-AVERAGE HOUSEWIFE

The More-Than-Average Housewife who, as we have seen, had almost been obsessed with the problem of orgasm, expressed her feelings during that experience in these words:

It is hard to describe what the orgasm feels like, but I'll try. In the first place, it's not like anything else that I could compare it with: I'm floating. I'm completely oblivious to my surroundings. Even if one of my kids should walk in at that moment, I don't think I could stop for a few seconds until I regained my thinking. . . .

I am in the most exquisite trance imaginable. It comes from way down and goes all the way up my back into my head.

I bite him. I can't help it. Only after I've come a couple of times do I try to think not to hurt him.

I sort of groan, and yet it's a different kind of sound. . . .

Now I'm off and running for anywhere from four to eight or ten orgasms. Usually five or six. They take about one minute.

My head spins . . . I feel exhausted. I'm flying. It's perfect, supreme, it's everything. . .

My husband doesn't need to do much now, but maybe he'll whisper something nice to me. I too don't have to work so hard at this time.

I tingle throughout my whole body. . . .

The orgasms vary from beginning to end. Sometimes the first and second are best, or maybe the third or fifth, or the second and the sixth. I never know. However if I go to ten, sometimes they fade. Rarely do I ever seem completely through.

Our informant's statement clearly indicates that for her the experience of orgasm was so intimately tied up with the phenomenon of *multiple* orgasm that she could not possibly describe the one without reference to the other.

In the light of this capacity for multiple orgasm, her last statement, "Rarely do I ever seem completely through," takes on a different meaning. It does so especially if we compare it to statements made by her in other connections in which she admitted her wishful fantasy of having not one, but two or three highly potent men around the house to keep her happy!

It is this sort of thing which has given rise to the conviction, frequently voiced by men, that contrary to all outward appearances, women's sexual capacity is in reality without limit. There is, of course, as we have pointed out, some basis in reality to this impression. Women are more capable of sustaining prolonged sexual activities than men: "Do you wives think," the exacerbated Iatmul husband as quoted by Margaret Mead demands to know, "that I am made of iron-wood that I am able to copulate with you as much as you want?"

How many successive orgasms is any woman capable of? In general we would say that the majority of women will reach the outer limits of their physical endurance after a maximum of, say, ten or twelve successive orgasms. Beyond this, most women tend to become hypersensitive and cannot tolerate sexual stimulation any further.

There are, however, reports of women who have stated that they experienced a much greater number of orgasms. We know of the case of a woman who claimed to have experienced over one hundred orgasms during a period of less than an hour! But we are inclined to believe that in many instances women reporting on such high numbers of successive orgasms may mistakenly refer to peaks of mounting tension and release which can occur during a prolonged plateau phase and not to genuine orgasms in the clinical sense.

THE SEXUAL SOPHISTICATE

What did our Sexual Sophisticate think of multiple orgasm?

I usually am satisfied with one orgasm, but I still like to go on and have several, if my partner doesn't mind. There are times when one orgasm seems to just stimulate me to go on and on for more.

After the first orgasm, my genitals become very sensitive, so that the second orgasm comes faster, takes less effort, and usually is quite intense.

In other words, she was capable of experiencing and enjoying multiple orgasm, but did not place nearly as much importance on this capacity as did the More-Than-Average Housewife.

THE MARRIED LESBIAN

When we asked our Married Lesbian the same question, her reaction was one of sheer incredulity about the whole matter of multiple orgasm. She had never experienced it, and even doubted its existence:

> I have never had what you call multiple orgasm. I am told— my husband tried to convince me—that some women have many orgasms, and—again, I very much doubt this. . . . I doubt that anyone's nervous system is capable of having ten orgasms in one evening.
>
> After an orgasm, I feel just good. I want to go to sleep. It's like I've been hit over the head. That's why it's very hard for me to believe that people can be coming, coming, coming. . . .
>
> I can see, maybe twice—once in the morning and once at night—but it really would be quite hard for me.

If we look back over what our informants have told us about their personal experience of orgasm, one thing stands out above all else: the *physical* need for the discharge of sexual tension is paralleled by an equally powerful *psychological* drive toward orgasm.

For at least two of the women whose sex histories we have quoted, the achievement of orgasm was of paramount importance, and for one (the More-Than-Average Housewife) her entire adult sex life seemed to have been centered around this problem.

But why should women, and only *women* have this difficulty in achieving a satisfaction that should be almost automatic? What in fact, does it mean if one speaks of women "achieving" orgasm? It implies, as Margaret Mead suggests, that women may have something more to *learn* in order to accomplish that which most men not only find easy, but far too easy.

On the other hand, while the female orgasm may indeed involve a greater number of learned responses than that of the male, the lesson cannot be too difficult, if one considers there are records of little girls masturbating to orgasm before the age of three! We are therefore convinced that the key to the problem of the female orgasm lies primarily, as both the anthropological as well as the physiological data would indicate, in the application of effective stimulation techniques (provided there is no emotional blocking, whether due to cultural or personal influences that might prevent the woman from responding to such stimulation). Otherwise, if the woman is properly stimulated, she will experience orgasm, and will experience it in at least nine cases out of ten just as easily as the man.

For some, this solution may sound too simple to be believed. However, the scientists who were able to experiment with these matters in clinical surroundings have proved the point we are here trying to make, to our own complete satisfaction. They insist that almost every physically normal woman could be brought to orgasm by devoting thirty minutes of teaching time to explain to her the most effective stimulation techniques and by letting her experiment with them.

Even if one has to admit that the woman who volunteers or is ready for such experimentation cannot be the most inhibited type, the result is still astounding. What undoubtedly helped was that the presence of the doctor and the whole clinical setting gave the female subjects official permission to go ahead and try what they would normally not dare to do in fifty years of marriage!

Incidentally, effective stimulation for one woman need not produce the same results in another, although in most cases it is some variation on the clitoral theme. More often than not, this is so, even where the woman requires vaginal penetration and is not even aware of the clitoral factor.

The trouble is that women do not experiment sufficiently on their own with stimulation techniques which may lead to orgasm. They almost always expect—as our Sexual Sophisticate said—a Prince Charming to come along and provide the miracle for them. This passive waiting-for-the-thing-to-happen shackles women to the extent of making them dependent on others for their sexual liberation, while preventing them from finding out on their own what methods of stimulation actually work best in their case. But unfortunately the very idea of being her own subject and experimenter in a serious effort of this nature is still emotionally beyond the powers of most women.

The fact that such experimentation is still unacceptable to many women is all the more regrettable, since women who do feel free to experiment in this manner, far from becoming addicted to auto-erotic practises, as is often feared, generally have a much easier time in their heterosexual relations. In addition, the woman who has found her own independent way to orgasm is also much freer in her choice of a partner. For her it is never "the only man who can satisfy me" to whom she may become sexually enslaved. Her selection of a mate is based on other factors, possible only because she has gained greater maturity and confidence in her own sexual adequacy.

VII

Women and Pre-Marital Sex

SURPRISINGLY enough, only about half the American women of the present generation seem to enter marriage with any previous experience of intercourse. The other fifty per cent still approach married life, if not without any prior sex experience, nevertheless technically as virgins.

In England the figures for women with pre-marital intercourse are slightly lower, hovering around forty per cent plus for those born between 1914 and 1934.

In France and Germany, in the absence of comparable statistics, we would judge that a slightly, but not much greater proportion of women than in America are likely to have had pre-marital intercourse, and the same seems to hold for the Scandinavian countries, with the only possible exception of Sweden, where the incidence of pre-marital relations appears to be relatively high.

Almost more interesting than these figures is the discovery by Kinsey and others that most of the women by far who have tasted of the forbidden fruit before acquiring the necessary official sanction, have *no regrets* about it, including even the majority of those who had become pregnant in the course of their pre-marital activities. Not many even voiced regret at having undergone the sad experience of illegal abortion! (This, incidentally, was borne out by the attitudes of three out of our four main informants who had experienced artificial interruptions of pregnancy.)

It may astonish some to hear researchers agreeing that by

and large the girls who *do*, turn out to be better wives and more satisfactory lovers than those who *don't*, particularly if their pre-marital experiences have been satisfactory. According to Kinsey's study those who had *not* experienced orgasm before marriage, failed to do so after marriage *three times* as often as those who did have orgasmic experience before marriage.

Of our four chief informants, two, the More-Than-Average Housewife, and the Married Lesbian had had *extensive* pre-marital experience.

THE MORE-THAN-AVERAGE HOUSEWIFE

The More-Than-Average Housewife came near being seduced at the tender pre-Lolita age of ten.

This is how she herself sees these events in retrospect:

> The first time I almost had a man occurred at the house of a friend of mine who was separated from her husband. She had a daughter about seven and I was ten. She had a beautiful home, lots of men-friends, and everybody was having a good time. She let me spend several nights there, probably to keep the seven-year-old out of her hair. I felt she was sleeping with several of the men that came and went and I loved the excitement of the house.
>
> One night she was having a big party and this dark-type guy about thirty got me into the bedroom, kissed me and was hard and had it out. I can't remember whether I played with it, but I doubt it. Everything went so fast, as he was afraid my friend would catch him. He got on me and while I was very interested (curiosity, I believe) I was scared, so I tried to get away. I jumped up; he threw me down, and I said, "Leave me alone, or I'll scream for Janice and she'll never let you in again." That stopped him. He kept pawing me later, and since I was afraid, I told Janice to keep him away from me, which she did.

What strikes one immediately is that this married woman with a daughter of only a little more than her own age at the time of these events, is not looking back in anger. Nor is she criticizing her older friend for having exposed her to these experiences. Instead, she reports on them soberly, factually, and not without a touch of nostalgia for the good times that were had by all.

We next hear about her relationship with a boy of about her own age. Though appearing much more harmless than her experience with the older man who attempted intercourse with her, this boy's later rejection of her proved to be more traumatic than the former incident:

> The boys we dated, at camp, were three among a hundred gals. One of them fell for me and I for him. He was my first puppy love. We sneaked out nights, three boys and three girls, and hiked the mountains, swam nude and necked and petted. All very romantic, and I was thrilled to have someone show so much interest in me.
>
> I did not have intercourse with him, but was ready—boy was I ready!
>
> Several years later I got the biggest blow when he told me he was quitting me, because I was too forward and willing. That hit me like a ton of bricks. I suppose it was his honor holding him back, but I believe *he hurt me worse by being such a Puritan than if he'd taken me*. I believe it gave me an inferiority complex; he made me think I was not desirable.

Sad learning experiences like these frequently convince younger girls and even adult women that it is not safe to be too forward or show too much interest in sex. As previously stated, many men in our society still separate all females either into the group of angels, or that of she-devils. For example, many of the college men whom we interviewed for another study told us that they would never marry a girl who had gone to bed with them or had shown herself too eager (*Sex Histories of American College Men*).

Still talking about events during her early teens, our informant tells of the mixture of curiosity and fear which she felt during an experience with a young man about ten years older than herself:

Meanwhile I was flirting around the fellows at the beach. Necking under the dock, kissing under water and such. Then the lifeguard started showing me attention which I liked and finally he took me home one afternoon. We petted and necked and he felt me all over outside of my bathing suit. He tried to take my bathing suit off, but somehow didn't manage.

I was about twelve and I didn't trust this all-brawn-and-no-brain man (he was about twenty-five), but was *curious*.

All I remember of him is that he was big and hard and fast. He tried . . . I wiggled out from under. . . . Afterward I was scared as hell to go home, but I did. I never fooled around with him again.

Even in this instance, we see that as a young girl she had been at least as seductive as the older partner. This is a factor which is usually overlooked in public discussion of assaults against younger girls. In these cases, the man is generally considered as the sole aggressor and guilty party. The younger girl participant is, on the other hand, merely regarded as his unwilling victim.

Our informant's role in these affairs with older men becomes even clearer from her own account of the events which followed. In that section of her sex history she describes how she was getting ready for more serious sexual relations at about that time (she was still only fourteen):

I can't remember the exact time I actually first had intercourse, or with which one . . .

I had been participating in a lot of heavy necking, deep kissing, and so on. A boy would kiss my breasts and play with me, and I'd play with him; no more.

Then along about fourteen, my mother let my sister and me double-date with some respectable older men she knew. They were about thirty; old to us.

They gave us a big time, took us to fancy restaurants, shows, etc., and *we loved it!*

I thought a lot of one of the fellows, but he always kept at necking and never went beyond.

Then I met Bob, a piano player in a local club. I was about fourteen, and with him I went all the way.

I liked it. I guess he must have been the first one (if I had any virginity to lose, there must not have been any pain to it, or I'd remember it).

Perhaps I could have been satisfied without any intercourse; I don't know. All I do know is, he was swell to me. He gave me excitement: got me into the club by telling the boss I was eighteen. I'd sit at one of the front tables with a highball, watching him play in the band; dancing with him. It made me feel like a big-shot.

My folks liked Bob and trusted him. They didn't object to my going out with him. In fact, everybody liked him, including myself!

We used to have sex in his car or in the woods . . . I don't remember why we quit; I suppose he went to another town for a job.

I remember missing him and intercourse when he was gone, but I got over it.

He had boosted my ego and made me forget about the blow which the other fellow had given me with his talk about my being too fast.

What is one to make of accounts like this? All one's conventional reactions tell one that such things as our informant is describing of her adolescent years are altogether wrong. Everything in our upbringing insists that things of this sort should never have happened; that they are immoral, dangerous, and harmful to the young person concerned.

But what are the facts?

The facts, as far as one can see from our informant's report, bear out none of these assumptions. They show no evidence of psychological damage whatsoever to this woman. At least we know from the rest of her personal history that she became a splendid wife to her husband, a devoted and tender mother, and a law-abiding, responsible citizen.

Still, one cannot pass lightly over issues like these which entail so many questions of mental hygiene, moral values, and medical considerations.

Even the most liberal parents and the most forward-looking clinicians usually draw the line at precisely this point;

and with good reasons. Among these is the harsh reality that adolescent girls can get pregnant if they have sexual intercourse. And though pregnancy is not the unavoidable outcome of such early relations (as, for instance, the case of our informant shows), it constitutes a very real threat to the psychological and physical well-being of the young girl.

This kind of double threat will exist as long as social conditions and community attitudes in most Western nations remain more or less what they are today. That these conditions might well change in the future is made very likely by the example of Sweden. In that country, both the unmarried mother and her child are protected from social ostracism and other problems of illegitimacy.

But the fact that illegitimate and often unwanted pregnancy, together with an apparent rise in the veneral disease rate among teen-agers, are now plaguing that country, goes to show that the problem is still far from being solved. What seems to be needed (instead of the futile attempts at retrenchment that some Swedish physicians have recently advocated) is more effective disease prevention (in a non-punitive, non-moralistic atmosphere), more instruction in and easier availability of birth control measures for that age group, and finally the development of a new sex ethics, based not on religious precepts, but on those psychological and sociological principles of human conduct upon which most reasonable people (regardless of their particular religious creed and affiliation) can agree.

Meanwhile, cases like that of our informant are no more than lucky exceptions who happen to escape the usual social punishments for sexual precocity. Yet, sex histories showing early sexual development and activity are not nearly as infrequent as one might assume. In all the larger urban areas of America and Europe (and not only in Sweden!), sexual activities of adolescents appear to be rather on the increase. England, for instance, reports for the year 1961 another increase in the number of unmarried mothers which was especially marked in girls *under seventeen* (The London *Times*, December 14th, 1961).

Adolescent sexuality seems to be particularly widespread in the top upper and lower social and educational groups. In these classes, parents may no more approve of adolescent sex activities than middle-class parents. But they nevertheless *expect* both adolescent girls as well as boys to engage in them anyway. It is in that light that we must see the permissiveness of our informant's parents who obviously must have closed one or both eyes in allowing their daughter to go out with older men.

The next section of our informant's personal history spans the gap between her childhood and adult life. It includes comparisons between the advantages and disadvantages of older as against younger lovers for a girl of the in-between age. For the first time also, the problem of *orgasm* makes its appearance in her record:

> After the pianist I dated high school boys and necked along —once in a great while I went all the way. It was good, but a car is not ideal and an infantile man or boy is not much help to a girl trying to find that all-important *orgasm*. Still, I must have had some satisfaction, or I'd have called it quits. But I do know I always preferred older, more considerate, more experienced men.
>
> Anyway, about that time I met an Annapolis football hero. He was built like everything I liked. I worshipped him like a fool. We dated and smooched heavy quite a few times. On his last night we went all the way, quick-like, in a car. That ended that—he was career minded!
>
> Then I dated a few jerks for the fun. Several had cars and money to toss around on me. It was fine, but nothing more.
>
> They tried, but they didn't particularly appeal to me. Then graduation: I had a jerk for a date, wishing all the time it was someone else. After that, business school and a job.
>
> I started dating a fellow by the name of Jim about this time. He was a sweet kind of kid, shy to a painful point. He spent all his earnings on me. I went with him about two years, once a week. I could hardly stand to kiss him, but hated to hurt him.

He never tried to go very far; honor, I guess. I don't believe he ever had an erection with me, maybe he was coolish. He wanted me to marry him, but I knew it would never work.

A short time later, I dated another guy who worked in a bank and who didn't send me either.

Then I dated a boy my age who came closer to helping me get orgasm than anyone had done so far.

All this time I am making love on my back with the man on top. This guy tries it, and I get my legs up. This helps. I didn't get on top yet at that time, because in the first place, I figured he'd think I knew too much (remember I was still only about eighteen). Or maybe I just didn't think of it, or hadn't read about it yet.

How in the hell I never got pregnant all that time, I'll never know! They used French letters mostly, I guess, but I know sometimes they didn't. I can remember wishing I had someone to ask "What can I do to protect myself?" But I didn't dare.

It is typical for that age group not to worry seriously about pregnancy. On the other hand, our informant was at times much concerned about the problem and desperately wanted to talk to somebody about contraception. Unfortunately, there was nobody she knew at that time who could have helped her or in whom she had sufficient confidence. (If so, she might have been spared the later trauma of an unwanted pregnancy and its interruption.)

During the period covered by the next section of our informant's history, America had entered the war, and the military situation was beginning to color her outlook. In fact, during the mobilization, she had enthusiastically joined one of the women's auxiliaries of the armed forces, only to become more and more disillusioned and almost embittered as time went on.

It is therefore not surprising to find her by the end of the war ready to shed her uniform and resume civilian life with the definite hope of settling down to a more peaceful kind of existence. At that crucial stage in her life, she met her present husband, to whom at the time of this interview she was married for over fourteen years.

We thought it best to present our informant's own narration without interrupting it further by intermittent comment. Thus, the particular quotation which follows is considerably longer than any other in this study. However, we felt that this is indicated in order to preserve the continuity of her report and to convey the full impact of her experiences in the service and the events leading up to her marriage:

> Next I fooled around with one of the salesmen in the empty office where I worked. He had an erection, but since I was afraid to get into office entanglements, I just masturbated him and told him to leave me alone. He did, because he was married, but kept rubbing against me every chance he had. I just figured he spelled trouble, so wouldn't go out with him, although he kept wanting me to.
>
> About that time I'd been to Washington, D.C. and met the love of my life through a girl friend. We visited each other whenever we could, wrote passionate letters, and got engaged. We spent a week together. *We had intercourse about five or eight times each twenty-four hours.* I was about twenty and he twenty-three. We used every position, except I still didn't get on top, or I can't remember. But if I had, it seems like I'd have reached that Cloud 9, because I really intended to marry this fellow. *I loved him.* I liked every minute and believe I had a *half satisfaction.* He was about everything I wanted, but I suppose there was still doubt in my mind, and for sure there was some doubt in his about something. About a year later, we mutually called the whole thing off.
>
> I then dated a traveling salesman. He was a great guy with money and liquor flowing when he came to town. My folks liked him. He sent me gifts and flowers and sort of hinted at marriage. He suited me well on the surface.
>
> He invited me to a convention in another town, and I went. We had adjoining rooms and a few drinks, and soon we were in bed before the banquet that evening. He had me all fired up and then all he wanted me to do was perform fellatio on him. I never had done that before and for some reason wouldn't. That was all he seemed to want, so there I was, fired up and he wouldn't give me any, and I was damned if I was going to do what he wanted. I think it was repulsive to me. So I think I said, "I'll masturbate you, but damned if I know why I'm that

kind to you with the mood I'm in." I believe he said something like, "No thanks."

He stormed and fumed, while I had a few drinks, and I guess I was loaded by banquet time. All I remember is I got sick at the banquet and embarrassed hell out of him. He brought me up to bed, and I slept it off.

Meanwhile I suppose he went clubbing with his friends. Next morning I felt like a fool and was sorry about getting drunk. He said "O.K.," and we parted unloved and unfriendly.

Now we send Christmas cards to each other. He's married and has two kids.

I still can't figure him out. Probably he was a lot more knowing than I and tried to show me the way. If so, why didn't he explain a little, or tell me why he wanted it? But, if I had done what he wanted, and he'd come and had not gotten another erection, I'd still have been up the creek without a paddle.

After that, I got a job as a bookkeeper and secretary to a hardware store owner and politician. He was about fifty, stout and full of fun. He was eager to get at me. Naturally, his wife hated my guts, probably because she'd never given him a good one and was afraid I would.

I had a few drinks and kissed him one night. Then he took me on a convention. He enjoyed having the men think he was getting it from me. He kissed me and we lay side by side nude, but I told him I was staying true to somebody else as I intended to marry him. So I only masturbated him, and since he didn't appeal to me, I just sort of stayed half frustrated. From what I saw, I don't think he could have done me much good anyway.

Then I decided I wanted to see California. The war was on. I had fun on the trains and buses going out. I met soldiers and sailors and dated a few, but nothing more.

I remember one carfull of soldiers, half loaded and I was the only girl. We played football and they let me referee. When a few of them started acting like they were going to rough me up into a rape case, one real nice brute, I guess so big they were a little afraid of him, took me under his protection. We horsed along and no one bothered me, because he wouldn't let them. Then their car was unhooked and sent somewhere else.

Oh, I forgot, before I went West I had met an army officer. I fell for him, but quick, and when he was in town we dated, then laid, and when he was shipped to another base, I went with him too.

My sister who had dated him before me and who had introduced us, told me later that she thought he was married. I didn't know it at first, until I was gone completely nuts on him. Then he told me, after I truly thought I'd found the right guy for me.

I stayed with him for a week or two. He was shipped overseas. He was the best in bed yet—or I was improving. *I believe once or twice I had orgasm with him*, although I still hadn't crawled on top. But by putting my feet on his shoulders and the fact that he seemed to have one of the biggest ones I'd had, I guess I made it.

Later I was afraid I was pregnant. I told him and we had a big discussion what to do. The next thing I knew he took leave before finding out for certain whether I was pregnant or not.

Then I went with a soldier whose brother was a big politician in the state. He had a summer cabin and a car. He used to give cabin parties and the liquor was flowing. As I recall, when we finally got to bed, he wasn't much either. We had a small car accident and I decided to get away from the heavy-drinking crowd. Besides, he wasn't satisfying me. So I said bye-bye.

After that I started going with a soldier whom I really liked. He found a radio trailer on the base which was in a good secluded place. Occasionally we also made love in one of the airplanes that were sitting around on the runways.

This guy came about as near as anyone to satisfying me. We talked of marriage, but he had some dream girl virgin to marry at home. I told him, "Go to her, but I bet you'll never get it as good as you've got it right now." He said he'd never marry anyone but a virgin. I hope to hell he married six of them and never got a decent piece of tail!

After that I just drifted along for a while from one fellow to another. Then, out of sheer spite I started dating an officer I knew that the bitch of a commanding officer wanted for herself.

One day, about twenty of us swam nude and he worked me into a lather. Then he said, "I'm married, I adore my wife, I don't want to hurt you, her, or myself. So I'm calling it quits right now before we go too far." There I was left high and dry that night, even though I knew he was ready and so was I. I couldn't quite figure him out. Perhaps he really hadn't cheated on his wife so far and didn't want to break his record.

Then I dated a sweet, cold, inhibited guy for a while who wanted marriage and that was all. I didn't want to get married then, at least not to him. (During all this time I'm still writing to the married guy overseas, telling him I'll die until he gets back. He writes me the same crap.)

Next I dated a fellow who was beautifully built and had about the biggest penis I've ever seen in my life. He was also the most passionate man I ever saw. I don't remember ever standing by him in a crowd or looking at him that he didn't have an erection. If I masturbated him to orgasm, he was ready to go again five minutes later. I'd do it again and the same thing would happen as before.

I sure regret never getting more than that, but we were on the post. He pleaded, begged with tears in his eyes to have it anywhere, even ten feet from the officers' club, but I was afraid we'd be caught with so many people coming and going. He begged me to perform fellatio on him, but I still couldn't bring myself to it. Besides I was a little afraid of him: he was so strong, irrational, passionate and stupid, and did impetuous things when aroused (which was most of the time!).

We just kept petting and played with each other. Then he begged me to let him perform cunnilingus on me. I had never had that (I haven't yet, but wish now I had let him). I didn't let him, because his fierce passion scared me. I believe he'd have laid me anywhere, in the middle of dress parade, even if he knew his head would be chopped off for it.

I felt I was either going to be swamped by this fellow or call it quits. Since he was also insanely jealous and I was afraid of him physically, I told him to find someone else. I couldn't stand his torture any more.

I bet he'd make a great husband, if he ever learned to calm his passion down a little and if he'd ever leave you alone long enough to get some sleep. I should have tried it. He had cave-man tactics. A little of that goes a long way with me. I need a man who can hold his passion and stay erect for a long time.

Next I dated a boy who was back from overseas. He was a fascinating talker, interesting and intelligent. We kissed and I had sort of taken him away from my girl friend who had told me she had slept with him. He was a newspaperman before the war. He was older than most of us and just seemed to look on us as kids. I think he liked me a lot to talk to, but didn't seem to want more. He didn't particularly send me. I think the war and killing he had seen had had a profound effect on him. He seemed to want to go back to war and get killed. I felt a great compassion for him. He wouldn't go with my girl friend again, and she blamed me and swore I had slept with him, which I hadn't.

My next boy friend was a sweet kid whom I met a week before he was being shipped overseas. He told me he knew he'd be killed and he was so scared, scared, scared. I'd have given it to him, just because I felt so sad for him. The damn war. The injustice of it all. He cried and I hated wars for sure. But he never tried. I don't suppose he'd had any yet, and he did get killed. He was so young and sweet and kind.

By this time I hated my commanding officer's guts, was sick of the place where we were stationed, and goofed off good and proper.

I dated an old army man. He couldn't live anything but army life. He was a hard drinker, tough, cynical, and about forty years old. The first night he was nice. The next night he was pretty drunk and tried rape out in the middle of nowhere. I didn't particularly care for him. The rape attempt made me mad and I decided for sure he wasn't getting anything from me, the cynical bastard. So he damn near choked me to death, but somehow I got loose. I started walking, and I walked three miles home. He kept trying to give me a ride, but I was afraid to get in the car. He kept wanting me to date him, but I didn't. He was insane when he couldn't have it, but I felt I was too young to die. Besides, I didn't like him enough.

Soon after I got out of the service, I met the fellow who is now my husband. By then I was getting ready for marriage, and I guess he was too—so everything clicked.

It almost didn't click, though, when I met the married guy from overseas—he just about bowled me over again. But I got the idea that this guy had been feeding me a line by mail for two years. He wanted the wife and me as mistress on the side. That's when I decided it's not for me, not any more, at least. So I tell this poor, misunderstood married Joe that it's breaking my heart, but I'm marrying Steve. And I thank whatever gods may be that for once I used my brain instead of tail, for even if the other guy had divorced and I'd married him, it would have been tough sledding, and wouldn't have worked.

So we were happily married with all the church stuff and frills (for the parents), and all I wanted was to live in bed, and Steve too. I didn't even know it was sacrilegious to be married in white, unless you're a virgin which my husband's sister later told me with a sneer.

All I can say is that I believe my folks were thankful I was at last settling down and doing it legal like, and I think his Mom was too, although she'd never say it.

The presentation of a sex history like this can, of course, hardly help but give the impression that the woman whom it concerns was an irresponsible, promiscuous individual. This is however not at all the case. We must bear in mind that she accepted without question the naturalness of her powerful sex drive and with that acceptance the need to seek fulfilment of it. Equally strong in her was the need to care about the man who could give her this fulfilment. These twin drives formed the broad basis of her constant experimentation: again and again she abandons a lover to try another when one or the other of her basic needs is frustrated.

There is a third aspect to consider in her favor: a woman, such as our informant, inevitably encounters and has to bear the brunt of the double standard—many of the men who were eager to enjoy a sex relationship with her were, precisely for that reason, unwilling to commit themselves to the respectability of marriage.

It is noteworthy that she, on the other hand, tried uselessly to maintain an attachment with the man with whom she felt she was in love, giving up only when she came to the realization that "he wanted the wife and me as mistress on the side." It is surprising that our informant did not become bitter and cynical under these circumstances, but maintained her good-natured and cheerful attitude.

Looking back over the material which she provided, one may be somewhat surprised to hear her claim that during one of her pre-marital experiences she had been having inter-course "about five or eight times each twenty-four hours." This sounds high and may be slightly exaggerated, though nevertheless possible. If it were factual, it would mean that she was having intercourse once every four to five hours. At the commencement of a new relationship and over only a short period of time this would not be too uncommon.

Turning to the other three women whose sex histories we have chosen for more detailed discussion in this study, we find that one of them (the Doctor's Wife) had had only one or two pre-marital experiences of lesser intensity than those of the More-Than-Average Housewife.

Of the two remaining subjects, the Sexual Sophisticate did not have many pre-marital experiences either, but her comments about them warrant their inclusion in this report.

The Married Lesbian, on the other hand, had had a large number of pre-marital contacts. Unfortunately, most of them were, as we shall see, rather negative or meaningless to her, and it was *her attitude* toward these affairs (rather than the acts themselves) which, from a mental hygiene point of view, would make them appear much more dubious than those of our previous informant.

THE MARRIED LESBIAN

In the following section she tells in our interview how she got deflowered and of her reactions to this first sexual episode in her life:

> When I was eighteen, the first man I ever went out with, I also went to bed with. Just did it in cold blood. I couldn't have been less interested. I wasn't interested in him and not inter-ested in it.
>
> He tried to be seductive, and I thought he was an awful ass, but that I might as well get it over with.
>
> The next day I went to see him. First I waited an interval of twenty-four hours in which I thought he might call me, but

he didn't. Then I got interested, of course. I got all dressed up in black . . . black dress, black stockings, black shoes, and went to see him. He asked me if I was in mourning for my chastity.

Question: What did your sex with him consist of?

Answer: The whole bad American bit . . . Face to face . . . quite painful, not a bit pleasurable. I was interested, yes, but I couldn't have been less excited . . . just sort of observing it.

Question: Had there been any foreplay?

Answer: All the foreplay was verbal.

Question: Did you use any contraceptive?

Answer: Not the first time. He used a contraceptive subsequently.

That reminds me of when I was about thirteen, I was visiting an aunt during the depression. The boy behind the soda fountain asked me for a date. I wasn't supposed to do this, but I did go out with him. We did a lot of necking on a park bench, and he said something to me about buying some rubbers. I had never heard of rubbers, and I pictured them as tires. I imagined something black and round. I knew what they were used for, but could never picture what they were really like. He said something about getting them at Sears & Roebuck's department store. All I can remember is having this picture of Sears with these mountains of black tires.

One can see immediately from the cynical humor with which she relates these incidents that they were just the kind of first sexual experiences one does not wish a young girl to have.

The marriage of her parents had been unhappy and was later dissolved. Her own unfortunate initiation could therefore only tend to reinforce the already negative impressions gathered in her parental home. Nor were her subsequent heterosexual experiences designed to correct this picture:

Very shortly after my defloration, I had another lover, whom I liked very much. I pursued him, as he was completely disinterested in me. Very desultory relationship. No pleasure; quite masochistic, but it had more continuity than the first affair. They were both short relationships and I didn't have orgasm. Both just as poor quality.

We notice that our informant did not achieve orgasm and, if we may take her literally, did not even have any pleasure in these relationships. (We would, however, assume that she must have experienced some degree of pleasure in the course of these sex activities.)

As bad luck would have it, she became pregnant as the result of one of these unsatisfactory encounters and had to have an abortion. Barely recovered, she began another round of similarly unhappy experiences:

> After I recovered, the same girl friend insisted that I travel to Chicago with a German musician who had fallen in love with her. His only interest in me, therefore, was the connection with my girl friend. Subsequently, I had an affair with him, which was completely cold-blooded. He was impotent. The moment he'd touch you—ejaculatio praecox.
>
> He didn't try it very often. It was too embarrassing for him. He was only interested in 69.
>
> I don't remember my part in it. No sensation, no pleasure. And this goes on for about twenty-five more lovers. I have had so many lovers in my life, I couldn't begin to enumerate them.

It would be merely repetitious and depressing to go into the details of most of our Married Lesbian's pre-marital relations. Still, she managed to rescue at least *one* satisfactory relationship with one of her lovers out of all the rest. Also, her Lesbian relationships were, as we shall later see, of a much happier and more rewarding type.

We cannot, however, leave the discussion of this woman's pre-marital experiences without some more general comment on mate-selection. From our own observations, it hardly ever fails that individuals with a family background like that of our informant begin their own sexual relations, so to say, on the wrong foot. It appears that their impressions about the unhappy nature of their parents' marriage predisposes them toward equally unhappy relations in their own lives.

At close range, one can frequently observe how this type of person goes about unconsciously selecting with uncanny accuracy one unsuitable partner after another. The only factor which all these outwardly sometimes very different love objects have in common is that they lend themselves extraordinarily well for the purpose of recreating the structure of the parents' marriage and the dynamics of their interaction.

In psychotherapy it is extremely difficult to break into this type of repetition compulsion. It is as if these unlucky individuals were driven by a power stronger than their own better knowledge and intentions. In this manner, they helplessly keep moving in a vicious circle of self-frustrating relationships, without being able to profit from their own painful experiences.

THE SEXUAL SOPHISTICATE

The pre-marital relations of our Sexual Sophisticate were, in contrast to those of the Married Lesbian, much more satisfactory, though considerably fewer in number. We shall first let her tell what she has to say about them, reserving our comments for the end of this portion of her sex history:

> As I told you, *sex was an area of life which was completely closed to me when I was young.* That I was sexually frustrated as most teen-agers are, I no longer refuse to acknowledge.
> My parents were kind and loving, but socially and sexually timid people who gave the impression they were almost sexless beings. They did not lay down any prohibitions about sex that I can remember. I can now look back and see that I had been as effectively imprisoned during adolescence by my own conscience as I would have been if I had been put in jail with a sign on the door, No Sex Allowed.
> Believe me, I suffered from this prohibition. I didn't dare to date, because I knew that first would come the kiss and then the insistence that we just go a little further. Since I was going to *stay a virgin for my future husband,* come hell or high water, the safest way was not to date, as I have always found it unpleasant having to refuse people.
> Well, I went through all of my high school with just a few

dates, limiting my social life to my girl friends. When I went to college, I became more daring and dated a little more frequently. But it was not until I graduated from college that I finally weakened to one man whom I had been dating steadily.

Really, I let myself be seduced on that occasion for several reasons. One is that I had almost come to the conclusion that I would not marry; so why save my virginity? Secondly, I was attracted to this man. He was loving and affectionate and desired me very much. So I had my first sexual experience more for his sake than because I was strongly sexually excited.

This lack of sexual excitement was partly due to the fact that I was not relaxed about sex and felt too inhibited and guilty to let myself enjoy it the first time. My boy friend was not the most adept lover either. But I came to enjoy all of my subsequent sexual experiences with him, even though I still was not having orgasm. It was strange. I gave up my precious virginity and accepted a sexual relationship with him, but still maintained my proper respectability, you might call it, with any other man I dated. The crowd in which we moved assumed we were sleeping together, as we were so close and spent so much time in each other's company. So at times when I dated some of the other fellows, they expected that I would go to bed with them too. But I was as monogamous as if I had been married to my steady lover.

I have to admit that I was attracted to some of the other fellows and would have liked to have sex with them. Today I feel that I ought to have had my head examined for having been so prudish. I realize now that all I was doing was merely trying to resolve my guilt about pre-marital sex. This I did by convincing myself that it was all right to go to bed with my steady boy friend whom I loved, but not to assume that this gave me the right to enjoy the other men as well.

My first affair lasted for about two years and we had sex regularly once or twice a week throughout that time. Our love-making was not very imaginative. We used mainly two positions: either he was on top and I was below, or I was on top and he was below. But sex was new to us and since we didn't live together, we were eager to make love and did not need the extra stimulation that variations can give.

When we broke up, I dated irregularly. I waited quite a long time before I went all the way with another fellow. This next lover was the man who first taught me about fellatio. I must admit that I was sexually never very active before I got married, and when I did start going to bed with a man, it usually was a long-standing affair. If I have any regrets at all about this period in my life, it is only that I limited my experiences as much as I did. My own self-imposed restrictions really served no good purpose, aside from salving my guilty conscience, and were not even too successful in that respect.

Looking at our Sexual Sophisticate's pre-marital history, she does not appear to be anything like sexually sophisticated from the outset. On the contrary, we find her coming from a sexually restricted milieu, with a good and wholesome family life, but without any pattern of active sexual behavior with which she might have identified. Interesting to note is her comment that, even though her upbringing had not been overly strict, her own self-manufactured prohibitions were all the stronger. This often happens in such cases: in the absence of clear guiding principles from the elders, the child is forced to assume that that which is not talked about is wrong; he then has to construct and impose his own code of behavior. Usually this turns out to be much more restrictively guilt-ridden than any obvious parental controls might have been.

We see that our Sexual Sophisticate at that time was still strictly monogamous. Like so many other women, she regarded her affair with her steady boy friend as a kind of marriage and rejected the approaches of all other men. This behavior she explained as being designed to appease her feelings of guilt about the fact that she was having pre-marital sex at all. Her self-imposed moral code, and this we consider of more general importance, was not motivated by a basically monogamistic disposition on her part.

Of course, one cannot draw final conclusions from a single case, or from four, or even a few hundred cases. But in addition to all other evidence, our informant's analysis of her own motivation does tend to discredit even more the myth of the supposedly monogamistic nature of women.

Comparing the pre-marital experiences of our chief informants, a picture emerges which indicates that the two women whose pre-marital experiences were relatively satisfactory (the More-Than-Average Housewife, and the Sexual Sophisticate) also had the more satisfactory marital relationships. In this we can include also the Doctor's Wife whose pre-marital affairs were perhaps not very important, but were nevertheless pleasurably toned. Naturally, the one woman who had the least satisfactory pre-marital experiences with men, our Married Lesbian, also had the most problematic marriage among these four informants.

The sex histories which we have considered in this section confirm therefore that the absence or presence of pre-marital experiences is in itself not the most decisive factor for the woman's later sexual adjustment.

Nor does the *quantity* of sexual experience seem to have a decisive influence on a person's future sex attitudes and behavior. This is particularly dramatized by the pre-marital experiences of the More-Than-Average Housewife and the Married Lesbian who, of the four, had the greatest number of pre-marital contacts.

The only thing that really *does* matter in the end is, as we have seen, the overall emotional and physical *quality* of the woman's pre-marital experiences. This factor does carry over into the future and profoundly affects her subsequent sexual adjustment and happiness. The More-Than-Average Housewife clearly demonstrated this point:

> *I do not know why I played so fast and loose,* except I was having fun. I remember saying to myself 'long about sixteen after dating a couple of boys who didn't arouse me whatsoever with their lack of technique, "so help me God, I'll never marry without trying him out first a few times!"
>
> I don't think I explained fully my sexual experiences before marriage. It seems so long ago, I can't remember the details too well, except whether the fellow was good at making love or whether he wasn't.

Unconventional and rebellious as our informant's sexual philosophy might be, she finds herself in excellent international company concerning her point of view. It has, for example, been advocated in America by Judge Lindsey in his well-known book, *Companionate Marriage,* as well as by Bertrand Russell in England, René Guyon in France, and many other leading American and European thinkers. Nor is trial marriage an altogether new concept; it was known and widely practiced for centuries in various rural areas of Europe, and to some extent even in frontier America.

In other areas of the world also, for instance, in Melanesia, Central India, and elsewhere, young people are allowed to form a large number of casual relationships before marriage. In the course of these temporary alliances, a certain mate selection gradually takes place and eventually leads to more permanent relations and marriage.

But returning to our More-Than-Average Housewife, we must ask ourselves the question, how does she herself appraise the effects of her pre-marital experiences in the long run? This is how she herself sees the first part of her life and its implications for her marriage:

On marriage: undoubtedly if I'd have married young I wouldn't have made love from one end of the U.S. to the other. But it wouldn't have lasted, unless my husband had had super-human strength—a man learns much with age too. If I had married young, I might have started having sex to see how the rest of the world went about it. Even so, I don't imagine I'd have settled to only one man anyway. You might say I got it out of my system and then took the best available man when I was ready—or maybe I didn't have too good a choice until I was ready. All I know is, I don't think I was ready or able 'til older. The main reason, I think, that I didn't marry early was because I was having one hell of a good time living it up and didn't want responsibilities and was looking for something which I eventually found. Anyway, *I doubt that I would live my life much different, if I had to live it again.*

She may be right. It was fortunate that she recognized her own needs and limitations. Had she acted otherwise, she might have brought much more serious trouble onto herself and in the process have involuntarily done harm to others. From a mental hygiene point of view, it is therefore all the more desirable that she felt no regret about her pre-marital experiences. Equally, the fact that she did not wish to have lived her life differently is a sure indication that it contained sufficient pleasure and emotional gratification to justify itself, at least in her own experience.

VIII

Women and Auto-Erotism

IF there is any sexual activity about which women worry more than any other, it is masturbation. Kinsey found that the "average" American woman was considerably disturbed for a long period of time about the idea of masturbation. Leaving aside for the moment the question as to why this is so, one finds, as one might have expected, that (not only in the Western world, but well-nigh universally) fewer women than men engage in masturbation.

Anthropologist Margaret Mead, on the basis of her studies of South Seas cultures, came to the conclusion that the reason for this sex difference is a purely anatomical one: "The female child's genitals," says Prof. Mead, "are less exposed, subject to less maternal manipulation and self-manipulation." For that reason, Prof. Mead suggests, in a culture where masturbation is not socially recognized and taught either by parents to children, or by older children to younger ones, the female child may simply never discover that her sex organs are subject to pleasurable stimulation.

Almost all known societies conform to this pattern with only a few exceptions, one such exception to the general rule being the Manchu society. In that central Asian group of people, anthropologist Weston La Barre reports, "it is quite customary for a mother to take the penis of her small son into her mouth and to *tickle the genitals of her little daughter* in petting them in public." (Italics ours.) Wherever a culture engages in these types of practices, one may expect that equally as many women as men would engage in masturbation.

On the other hand, it is surprising to learn that among married people, *wives masturbate more frequently than husbands*. Surprising as this may seem at first glance, it becomes less so after some reflection: first of all, married men have (thanks to the double standard) many more opportunities than wives for extra-marital sex outlets that are socially not nearly as unacceptable as in the case of married women. Secondly, as we have seen, fewer wives than husbands experience orgastic satisfaction in their marital relations (but almost always in their auto-erotic activities). For this one must blame not only ineffectual intercourse techniques, but also the strain of sheer overwork to which a large proportion of men in our type of society are subject during the day: coming home tired in the evening, many of these husbands seem to have barely enough energy left to watch television from a comfortable armchair, highball in hand, with romance relegated to such time on weekends as may be left after neglected family duties, hobbies, civic affairs, etc.

Another sex difference with regard to masturbation in our culture concerns the sources from which men and women learn about masturbation. Women usually find out about masturbation on their own, for instance, by reading books on sex education, marriage manuals, or by attending lectures (sometimes even those designed to warn against masturbation!). Men, on the other hand, are more likely to be introduced to masturbation through a male companion.

Some women evidently discover masturbation almost accidentally at times of intense psychological sex stimulation. Among the many women we interviewed for the purposes of this study, one contributed the following fairly typical report on this subject:

I've just been wondering the other day how I ever got started masturbating. It was sort of an accident. I first discovered how when I was about eighteen, as the result of reading a book. Not a book on sex—it was a novel, Richard Wright's *Native Son*. It's wonderfully well written. I was reading in bed and in a state of excitement over one of the chapters I started rubbing my genitals. When I achieved an orgasm, it came as a great surprise. I felt the effects of it all the next day ... sort of a swelled-up feeling in that area though it's never been like that since.

Other women may have more uniquely individualistic ways of discovering masturbation. Such was the case with another woman from our sample who tells about this experience as follows:

I started masturbating in my senior year of high school when I was about seventeen. It was so funny; one night I was trying to make a mask out of paraffin for my ceramics class. As I soon saw, this wasn't going to work. So I ended up with a scrap pile of warm wax, and you can guess what happened. I started out making a Kwan-Yen. I began by making this tall image, and suddenly I thought, "Oh, my, this might solve a lot of problems." Then I fashioned this rudimentary gismo; you might have called it a dildo. I used it the first time while it was still warm and went nearly out of my skull. I attribute a great deal of happiness and joy to it. It was a tremendous comfort to me until my mother, prowling around my room, found it one day. Then there was a big scene.

The passage is somewhat atypical in the sense that most women in our society do not use dildoes for purposes of masturbation. It is very likely that many of those who do use them, simultaneously employ clitoral stimulation as well. The same holds true for women in cultures where dildoes are frequently used. These women achieve orgasm in a similar way to those Western women who insert a finger into the vagina while stimulating the clitoris. Most women in the Western world, however, masturbate simply by massaging the clitoris, without deep insertion of fingers or objects into the vagina. On the other hand, quite a few women will at times put some fingers superficially into the vaginal outlet to provide for more pressure during masturbation.

We have the sex history of at least one woman whose only way of achieving orgasm was by rubbing her genitals against her husband's knee. Fixations like this on one special and unusual form of masturbation are generally due to early childhood experiences during which the little girl experienced particularly voluptuous sensations, or even orgasm. Frequently feeding, bathing, or toileting situations, even medical examinations, or the administration of enemas provide opportunities of this kind. The child then recapitulates later these sensations in her masturbatory technique or in the accompanying masturbation fantasy.

There are still other common forms of female masturbation: some women like to press their thighs together rhythmically, thereby exerting pressure on the labia and clitoris. The frequency of this type of masturbation is generally not recognized because it is inconspicuous and can be accomplished not only in the lying down position or sitting, but also while standing or walking. One woman has told us of masturbating to orgasm while riding horseback and using the pressure of her genitals against the front of the saddle for the build-up of sexual tension. Still another informant spoke of masturbating in her childhood by leaning forward and pressing her thighs together while riding on the bicycle. In this category belongs the report of a French observer who tells of women in a factory achieving orgasm while operating foot-powered sewing machines:

> . . . I suddenly heard one of the machines working with much more velocity than the others. I looked at the person who was working it, a brunette of eighteen or twenty. While she was automatically occupied with the trousers she was making on the machine, her face became animated, her mouth opened slightly, her nostrils dilated, her feet moved the pedals with constantly increasing rapidity. Soon I saw a convulsive look in her eyes, her eyelids were lowered, her face turned pale

and was thrown backward; hands and legs stopped and became extended; a suffocated cry, followed by a long sigh, was lost in the noise of the workroom. The girl remained motionless a few seconds, drew out her handkerchief to wipe away the pearls of sweat from her forehead, and, after casting a timid and ashamed glance at her companions, resumed her work. The forewoman advised her to sit fully on the chair, and not on its edge. As I was leaving, I heard another machine at another part of the room in accelerated movement. The forewoman smiled at me, and remarked that that was so frequent that it attracted no notice.

Quite a few women also masturbate while taking a bath by letting the stream of warm bath water from the tap run over their genitals, or by playing a flexible hand-spray over the genital region. Some women combine this technique with manual stimulation of the clitoris and vagina, while others prefer just to let themselves be stimulated by the running water. Said our female analyst, "I have had at least two women patients who used this technique. It's very nice, and the water helps too. Anyway, the bathtub is the most comfortable place to do it."

THE FEMALE PSYCHOANALYST

We also wished to check our own impressions about women's masturbation *fantasies* with those of the Female Psychoanalyst and inquired therefore what her clinical experience had been in that respect. To this question she stated:

I have found all kinds of masturbation fantasies in my women patients. Some have heterosexual fantasies, some have homosexual fantasies, fantasies about all kinds of intercourse positions, fantasies of sexual relations with animals, etc., I don't think there is any limit. . . . As far as the range of masturbation fantasies in the same woman is concerned, I haven't seen much of that. Usually they are pretty stable, pretty rigid, though with variations on the same theme. For instance, if a woman likes to think of being beaten, the beating can be done in many different ways, with the hand, with a whip, or by different people. But the basic beating fantasy remains fairly constant. Another patient may like to think of getting enemas and masturbates that way. One time, the enema may be given by a man, another time by a woman, as she may be forced to take it while being held by some people, like when she was a child. Or, a patient may have a heterosexual whipping fantasy which changes into an overt homosexual whipping fantasy and back again to a heterosexual one.

These observations of our Female Psychonalyst correspond closely to our own findings and those of other researchers. Kinsey, however, found that a little *over one third* of the women interviewed masturbated supposedly *without* any kind of fantasy, while only eleven per cent of the men did so.

Had most of her women patients masturbated at one time or another in their lives? we asked the analyst.

> Most of my women patients who have no sexual relations do masturbate more or less, though I have had patients who never did, not even in childhood.

We asked what her own experience with masturbation had been and how she felt about this form of sexual outlet from a mental hygiene point of view. To this she replied:

> I don't remember masturbating in childhood, except for preventing it by holding tight which has almost the same effect.

As to the other part of our question, she intimated that she herself had masturbated from time to time as an adult and that, contrary to some of her colleagues, she did not necessarily see anything wrong, pathological, or anti-social in it.

In this respect, we can only agree with our colleague. As far as we are concerned, we can see masturbation only as one among many possible sex outlets for women as well as men and see no possible harm arising out of it as such.

THE MORE-THAN-AVERAGE HOUSEWIFE

As to our other main informants, the More-Than-Average Housewife did not have much to say about the topic of masturbation. It did not play much of a role in her life and had never resulted in a single orgasmic experience. All she said about it was:

> I never masturbated as a child and just tried it a week ago. It only aroused me and made me urgently in need of sexual intercourse.

As a kind of after-thought she remembered an incident from her childhood:

> When I was a child of about nine, a girl next door had us over. She inserted a highball-mixer type of stick in herself and wanted my sister and me to do the same. I can't remember if we did. We told our mother and she told us not to go over there again.

THE MARRIED LESBIAN

Masturbation had by and large not been a major sex outlet for our Married Lesbian either. She had little, if any, recollection of childhood masturbation, other than that which had been incidental to certain erotic games. Later in life, masturbation became important to her only during a brief period shortly after her passionate affair with a girl friend by the name of Anne had broken up:

> I remember playing "doctor" with a childhood friend when I was about eight or nine . . . The doctor business got more serious when we were about ten. We got so far, we masturbated with pencils under the guise of taking temperatures . . . very pleasurable . . . I remember discovering masturbation as such when I was about sixteen. I tried it once or twice, but nothing much happened.
>
> Question: How did you discover it?

Answer: I don't know . . . I guess I was just remembering things that had happened earlier . . . I mean, playing with my brother, and the other games. I remember one afternoon deliberately going to bed and deciding to devote the afternoon to finding out how nice it was. . . . Taking a bath, washing my hair, and going to bed. It was very pleasant, but nothing happened.

Question: How did you masturbate?

Answer: Hands . . . clitoral.

Question: Did you experience orgasm?

Answer: I didn't have orgasm for years.

Question: How often did you masturbate?

Answer: Until I was eighteen, I masturbated once or twice a year. That's all. The only time in my life I really indulged myself in masturbation was the summer I left Anne. I had now discovered sex. It had become a necessity for me. I remember, that summer I spent practically the whole time masturbating . . . Twice a day, *with orgasm*.

The infrequency with which our Married Lesbian resorted to masturbation is to us an indication of her generally low sex drive, in spite of the fact that she had at times been sexually very active. (We feel that with rare exceptions, her sexual activities, especially with men, were otherwise motivated than by sexual interest.) It is all the more astonishing that masturbation did not become one of her favorite sex outlets since it had been one of the few sexual activities for her which apparently did lead to orgasm with some regularity. One can therefore only assume that other powerful psychic factors must have been present to inhibit this activity during most of her life.

THE SEXUAL SOPHISTICATE

Speaking about her own attitudes concerning auto-erotism, as well as the physical sensations and emotions accompanying it, the Sexual Sophisticate affords us rare insights into this seldom talked and written about subject:

I discovered masturbation rather late in life, in fact, I would be embarrassed to say how late. I had read about it and heard it mentioned many times before I overcame my moral compunctions and tried it. Even though I was never reprimanded, punished or even cautioned against masturbation, my family had managed without words to subtly impress on me a strong feeling that nice girls were not supposed to touch their genitals. I doubt that any degree of punishment could have so effectively deterred me from sexual experimentation as the mere desire to be liked, accepted and thought of as a good girl by those around me. Needless to say, I found masturbation enjoyable once I began. On the other hand, I can *not* say I was really ridden with guilt when I did begin masturbating, because before I attempted it, I had accepted the act as completely healthy and normal. I only recall feeling slightly embarrassed that if someone should find out, they might rightly conclude that I was more interested in sex than I was ready to admit at the time.

I have tried masturbating in several ways. I have found that the most efficient method by which I am able to reach orgasm more quickly than by any other, is the one in which I only rub the clitoris. Although my whole genital area is sensitized during masturbation and intercourse, still the most sensitive area for me remains definitely around the clitoris. I do not find it necessary to have anything in the vagina when I masturbate, not even at the moment of orgasm. Still I feel and enjoy the vaginal spasm and contractions in this way as much as during intercourse. Usually my masturbation is accompanied by fantasies, although this might at times not be any more realistic than the feeling that I have a partner with me. At other times, the fantasy can be quite elaborate at the beginning, but when I approach orgasm, it becomes a sensation of various shades of light, just as when I am having intercourse. I have never particularly liked my partner to masturbate me in foreplay. I prefer cunnilingus and feel it is more effective than manual play. But if my partner prefers to stimulate me manually, I do want him to insert a finger into the vagina during the clitoral play, contrary to my practice when I masturbate myself.

What interests us perhaps most in this informant's account is the fact that her elders had succeeded in getting across to her the idea that they did not approve of little girls touching their genitals, without ever having to make the point directly. As a result, she considered that area as taboo for her. She mentioned in this connection that what deterred her as a child most effectively from indulging in masturbation was *not* any threat of active punishment, but *fear of loss of love*!

This statement brings to mind a case conference at a famous child-guidance center in London. The analyst, a woman herself, mentioned in the discussion of her treatment with a pre-adolescent girl that the girl's mother had casually stated to her, "she had never had any problems to keep the girl's hands away from her genitals." The clinician had apparently let this statement of her young patient's mother pass without further notice. It is, however, just this type of casual comment which reveals the underlying phobic attitudes toward the sexual organs and the negative attitudes about sexuality in general that have been instilled in this insidious way. It was therefore not surprising to hear the therapist mention later and in a different context that this girl was already, at a pre-adolescent age, considered "priggish" and "moralistic" by her own peer group at school.

Interesting too in our informant's description of her subjective experience of masturbation is the fact that her vaginal sensations during clitoral masturbation were, according to her own statement, the same as during coitus. She substantiates thereby our contention that the "vaginal orgasm" theory is untenable and that intromission of the penis (or of any other object) into the vagina is of only secondary importance for the female sex response.

Looking at the problem of female auto-erotism from a more general point of view, we would consider the especially strong taboo against it is particularly regrettable for a number of reasons: first of all, it retards the erotic maturation of the young girl: secondly, the prohibition to touch the genitals (which is more emphatic and more seriously enforced in the case of the girl child) has a tendency to set up avoidance reactions toward physical pleasure (sensuality) in general, thus rendering the woman more prone toward frigidity; and finally, as already pointed out, the internalized prohibition to experience pleasure autoerotically inhibits experimentation and tends to make the woman unduly dependent on outside stimulation.

Aside from this, we suspect that the stronger masturbation taboo in the case of women is responsible for the fact that, as we have seen, a significantly higher percentage of women than men state that they masturbate *without* any accompanying fantasies. Rather than taking this phenomenon as a sign of women's lesser capacity for erotic fantasy, we are interpreting it as a manifestation of the higher degree of socially induced repression in the case of women (a factor to which we also attribute the lesser response of the majority of women toward a variety of psychological sex stimuli).

IX

Women and Extra-Marital Affairs

Most women who have extra-marital affairs have them in their mid-thirties and early forties. Possibly, one of the most potent reasons for this is that by their mid-thirties women have shed some of their inbred inhibitions and are freed to some degree from self-limiting negative conditioning. Circumstances are ripe for the strong but hitherto restricted, or even unacknowledged, sex drive to emerge. Greater maturity and experience open the way for exploration which youthful fear might have inhibited. Fear of another kind may indeed act as a spur—the feeling that time is running out. There is usually at this period greater leisure and more opportunity to pursue the fascinating possibilities of sex partners other than the somewhat time-worn husband who may, in fact, himself be seeking rejuvenation in the arms of twenty-year olds.

Whatever the reasons, or combination of reasons, by the time they reach the mid-thirties some one third of American wives can be counted on to have what statistical surveys like those of the Kinsey group call "extra-marital items" in their sex histories. In the absence of large-scale surveys as reliable as those of Kinsey in America one can only guess as to the amount of extra-marital contacts of women in various European areas. For England, there exist at present no comparable statistics on this question. Our impression is that the incidence figures of extra-marital contacts would approach those for America, with a tendency to fall slightly below.

In France, popular myths to the contrary, wives *as a group* should be expected to be no faster or slower stepping than anywhere else in the Western world. The difference there may be more in the *attitudes* toward sexual behavior in general and extra-marital affairs in particular, than in the behavior itself. French women (and men) might feel *less guilty* about their extra-marital affairs than say, American or British women. But it is unlikely that the little French woman of the bourgeoisie is more easily seduceable or less so than the housewife from Chelsea or Brooklyn, or, for that matter, the average married woman from Stockholm, Copenhagen, or Berlin.

After these international speculations, let us now examine the sex histories of our own informants to see what they do and think about extra-marital relations.

THE MORE-THAN-AVERAGE HOUSEWIFE

Starting with our More-Than-Average Housewife, we find her saying:

> I have loved my husband since we met and I believe he feels the same way about me. I have not cheated on him, so far, and don't expect to. However, I suppose if the opportunity arose, and I was really carried away, I might. But not as a lasting thing, a long drawn-out affair—no. Partly what keeps me on the straight and narrow is providing a good wholesome home for our children. I would not want to hurt my husband, children, or relatives by scandal.

This is a frank enough admission that if it were not for fear of scandal, she would have engaged in extra-marital relations. However, our informant describes how she likes to flirt with other men and how much she enjoys their attentions:

When we do go out to parties or socialize I usually talk to the men. They are interesting and more frank, besides *I like to flirt* with them. I dress well (for men) and believe I look pretty sharp, at least I don't notice them leaving my company until their wives get jealous and make them move on. Speaking of jealousy—we've never had any trouble there. This flirting and horsing around verbally is just a light game.

With regard to her flirting, she admits elsewhere that it is not nearly as innocent as it would appear, but that it gets her sexually excited. This is nothing unusual and lies in the nature of flirting itself. The remarkable thing about it is that in this case, the woman who is doing the flirting is perfectly aware of the fact that it is a source of erotic stimulation to her.

In her last statement, our informant also touches on the problem of jealousy. She says and believes that jealousy does not play any part in her marriage, but goes on to say:

The first weeks I got mad because his stupid mother gave the phone number of our hotel to one of his former bed-mates and that bitch called about two a.m. to cry on his shoulder about why he didn't marry her (I swear his mom did it out of spite). Then he got a long letter from Germany, a gal he'd met while a prisoner of war, stating that she was ready to come to him and the good old U.S.A. He too got mad at me once, because I got a couple of affectionate letters from a former boy friend. I had told him about it; and when the fellow came to town he raised such a stink about not wanting to meet him that I couldn't have him out to dinner or go into town for dinner with him.

It appears from this passage that the More-Than-Average Housewife and her husband are still a good way from having worked out the problem of jealousy. If it does not appear to be acute at present it is simply because neither one of them is, for the moment, giving much ground for jealousy to the other in actual behavior. But it might flare up and give them trouble in the future, especially if our More-Than-Average Housewife should give in to her temptation and start actually engaging in extra-marital relations. She herself seems to be at least partially aware of this possibility, and the awareness of it may be another less clearly recognized deterrent for her. This seems to be implied by the statement which immediately follows the previous one:

> Now that my husband has become a sales representative for his company, there is more chance for making love during the day or at night, depending on when he's home. He travels about a hundred miles radius; home most every night. When he goes on the road for a longer stretch and doesn't expect to be back for a few days, he takes care of me before he goes and upon his return. If he's gone more than a week solid, I get restless, nervous, and eager for a good lay. At present he's recovering from an operation and it's been three weeks and I feel like I'm going to bust out any moment if he doesn't get well enough soon. I now take care of his sexual desires manually and by fellatio, but for some reason, though he tries the latter on me too, it just frustrates me more. I need a man to crawl on top of and I'm afraid if I don't get one soon I'm going into the city some week-end and cheat for the first time (and I don't think he'd leave me for it, either!).

It is the last parenthetical phrase of her statement which makes us think that, in spite of her protestations to the contrary, she is not so sure whether any actual stepping-out on the husband might not break up her marriage.

In order to appraise this woman's desire for extra-marital contacts one must not see it merely as a temporary reaction to an unusual situation in her life (the husband's recent operation). Her whole pre-marital sex history speaks for the fact that in her case it must represent the expression of a rather more-than-average sex drive for a middle-class Western housewife (though we have interviewed a large number of women, both in America, as well as in Europe, with equally strong erotic needs as this informant).

As far as she is concerned, she had been used to having one affair after the other throughout her adult life and—as we shall presently see—she herself doubted whether any one partner could satisfy her sexual needs in the long run. How strongly she was tempted at this particular time comes across even better from the following statement:

> Also frustrating me now is the fact that his mother is with us. She's a sweet, kindly, bossy, dried-up widow of about seventy; she's been a widow for the past thirty years, is very religious, affectionate in a cold sort of way and a pain in the ass to me. She and I are at opposite poles—how in the hell a woman could do without sex for thirty years or even six months is beyond my comprehension. Well, anyway, when I'm in town today, I wish I could run into one of those good ones I left behind, enjoy a quickie and be back in time to fix supper.

If one could still ascribe these statements to the frustrating elements in her temporary situation, one could no longer do so considering the following afterthoughts to the previous passage:

> I think a woman should have three good husbands, at least that's what I need. I could gladly have sex with two men each night and love it. Well, dream on old girl, thank gosh they don't put you in jail for that. Since we've only been here six months and it's a small country town and I haven't met any men worth considering (except four unobtainable ones), I can't do much but go without—but believe me, in the future I don't intend to let myself get so high and dry again.

Statements like these give one an idea of the difficulties which this woman has in reconciling her married status in a supposedly strictly monogamous society with her own sexual needs and inclinations. She has a good idea herself of this potential conflict when she says:

> I'm glad I wasn't married during the war, I could not have stayed true to any man miles away, not even to this guy who is my husband and whom I love so much now. I also wouldn't

want him to do without sex, as I know he needs it for a sane, happy life.

In addition to these statements one must also take into consideration those made by our informant in another connection. There she stated that she and her husband had been talking about joining a group of other couples in the not-too-distant future with whom they might be able to exchange partners without running the risks of emotional entanglements (a trend which we have found on the increase among certain groups of urban couples, both in America, as well as in Europe).

The Doctor's Wife

Like our More-Than-Average Housewife, the Doctor's Wife found it difficult to refrain from extra-marital relations.

I haven't had any affairs since I got married, though I have all the freedom of going out and meeting other men. So, if I'm stimulated by another man during the day, my husband will just have the advantage of it in the evening. I don't think my husband has had any sex with anybody else either. I know of one time where there was some kissing involved, but I don't think he has had intercourse with anyone else since we were married. If he did, I think I would be very bitter about it, because this is something I feel is very hard for me to live up to. I sometimes feel very much stimulated by other men, and I think, if I can stand it, certainly he can, because there is enough satisfaction in our marriage to allay the necessity for such a thing. Anyway, the moment he should have an affair, I would have one too. There are many men around here that I wish had been around when I was single.

We see certain parallels between this statement of the Doctor's Wife and those of the More-Than-Average House-wife: both women were chafing at the bit, trying to hold onto a monogamous sex ethic which did not fully agree with their disposition; and both felt that under certain conditions they might have extra-marital affairs in the future.

The differences were that with regard to any possible future breaking of the monogamous code, the Doctor's Wife made her behavior conditional upon her husband's conduct; the More-Than-Average Housewife made it dependent only on the possibility of future deprivation and some assurance that it would not permanently damage her marriage or cause public scandal. Both women admitted their lively interest in other men, and neither of them expressed any views by which extra-marital contacts would be considered ethically unacceptable to them as such.

Up to the present, the two women had been able to sublimate their extra-marital interests in social flirting with other men. In the case of the Doctor's Wife, her husband had even added another dimension to her flirting. He actively encouraged her to do so, short of going all the way. To see his wife flirting with other men, or just to hear her report to him about it later, was a strong sexual stimulus to him. It made the wife's flirting an important element in their married sex life. This was the fuller meaning of our informant's statement that if she was getting stimulated by other men, her husband would get the benefit of it.

THE MARRIED LESBIAN

Our Married Lesbian, on the other hand, stated with equal candor that she was "not interested in other men, *one is bad enough*," and that she "couldn't care less" about having an affair at this point, but it was *she*, rather than the other two women we discussed, who had had extra-marital relations in the past! In order to understand this woman's short-lived flare-up of interest in extra-marital contacts, we must fill in some of the background which provided the motivation for her behavior.

After some time of marriage, it became obvious that she

was having difficulties conceiving. The couple consulted a Fertility Clinic and were given conflicting advice by the experts. One group was of the opinion that very frequent intercourse might yield the best results, while other doctors suggested a mixed regime of abstinence, alternating with high frequencies of intercourse during her most fertile period.

She tells of this trying period in her life with a sarcasm not altogether inappropriate to the situation:

> My doctor decided all my nervous symptoms were due to the fact I wasn't getting pregnant. So, he sent me to the Fertility Clinic, and they started working on us. We kept temperature charts and spent our lives copulating. Carl said this ruined everything for him. We seemed to spend our lives doing nothing but having intercourse. You know, without feeling, without desire, without anything . . . just to get pregnant.
>
> There was some difference of opinion among the experts as to the desirable frequency of intercourse around the time of ovulation. Some authorities felt every other night was ideal, others felt it was better to save up the sperm—it would make for better quality. But some people said, pigs did it extremely frequently, and it seemed to make the quality of the sperm even better. Since the authorities were undecided, there was not a minute that could ever be missed of this three or four day span. Nothing happened. In fact, the more of this enforced breeding, the less results. Then I got very mad at the doctors because I felt they were having a good time at our expense. That's how I decided I was going to do some experimentation myself. At that point, they decided to try artificial insemination, and it took immediately.

She then tells how "all this enforced copulating" had completed the ruin of her married sex life which, never having been very good to begin with, had been suffering from periodic spells of deterioration. It was at this time that she decided—as soon as the baby was old enough for her to leave —to go abroad and try to forget about it all:

The following year I went to Europe alone and really had a wonderful time. By then I had become quite frustrated and I felt I had to *justify* my womanhood. I was like a bitch in heat. I had four different affairs. Men simply followed me in the street. The first affair was with a man I sort of bumped into in a near-riot in Madrid. I was pushed up against him in the crowd and was suddenly looking up at this very handsome man. We started going out together. I remember being terribly excited by this man while dancing. I felt almost drugged. Next day he said he was taking me to his home. Instead, we went to a small hotel that existed solely for that purpose. People were waiting in line for rooms. The whole idea was more exciting than the performance. I didn't have orgasm. I didn't intend to, I'm sure. I loved the idea of not being able to talk. We knew absolutely nothing about each other.

I had two other affairs—both of them sexually indifferent, but very exciting, lots of fun. I became emotionally involved with a twenty-six-year-old—I was thirty-four at the time. *I came home feeling much better. It was the idea that I was still very attractive to people and could have a good time.* When I got home, I became pregnant again within a month. I was feeling good, gratified, I had had a good time.

What stands out immediately is that this woman's *motivation* for her extra-marital affairs was very different from that which the other two women had given as the possible cause of any future extra-marital contacts on their part. Neither of the other two women was speaking of frustration in the same sense that our Married Lesbian uses the term. When speaking of having been frustrated at the time of her European trip, our Married Lesbian was referring less to direct sexual frustration than to emotional frustration due to her husband's total neglect of her after the arrival of the baby.

One must remember that this woman's sex drive had always been on the low side, even when it was at its all-time high during her passionate Lesbian affair, or with her former one-and-only male lover. Her statement that during the time of her European trip she was "like a bitch in heat" must therefore be seen as a very temporary flare-up of sexual interest, motivated by psychic factors *other than sex*. It is, for instance, noteworthy that the idea of not understanding the language of the men with whom she had these affairs and not being able to talk to them acted as an additional erotic stimulus. Some women can find orgasmic satisfaction only with men who are removed from them in some way, by being a complete stranger, or socially inferior, by not having a common language, or any other situation that creates a barrier which enables the woman to relax with no permanent responsibility toward her partner and in which she can communicate only with her body, gestures, eyes, etc. This kind of arm's length contact is of course highly conducive to sexual fantasies which themselves also contribute their own excitement value to the situation.

We hear that the effects of these encounters, much as they may have left to be desired, were nevertheless highly therapeutic to our Married Lesbian. She returned home, feeling much better, reassured of her attractiveness to other people, knowing that she could still have a good time, if she wanted to, and apparently prepared to give her previously deteriorated relationship with her husband a new try.

THE SEXUAL SOPHISTICATE

Quite different in motivation and effect from the previous three informants and from all the rest of the women interviewed for this study, was our Sexual Sophisticate's position toward extra-marital contact. For her, extra-marital sex was not just something you might have because you are either bored, or frustrated, or to reassure yourself of your attractiveness to others: she simply did not believe in sexual monogamy! As we learned from her and as we were able to convince ourselves by intimate knowledge of the case, this woman had a deep and meaningful relationship with her husband. But to neither of them did mutuality of interests, friendship, affection, and even romantic love spell sexual exclusivity.

Considering our informant's particular marriage situation and feelings, we may be better able to understand what she has to say about extra-marital sex, though it may run counter to what is generally accepted and what is almost held sacred, alike by most of those who do and those who don't engage in extra-marital affairs:

> I was *hesitant* about having extra-marital sex as I did not want anything to disturb my relationship with my husband whom I love. But after several years of marriage we came to a decision which would allow us both to have sex with other persons, and since neither of us is the jealous type, this has worked rather well with us.
>
> I would *never dream of having a secret affair* behind my husband's back, as I think honesty and trust are the foundations of any good personal relationship and therefore certainly essential for marriage. I think it is important to tell my husband if I have been to bed with someone and with whom.
>
> Even though I have enjoyed these experiences, I have never been in love with any of the other men in the same way that I am with my husband, but I would never consider going to bed with someone I don't like.

After these frank remarks about her unorthodox personal sex ethics, our informant continues by giving us a practical example of what she means:

> Of course *I do not feel guilty about my extra-marital affairs*, because I would only feel badly if my husband did not know or did not approve.
>
> I had one of my most exciting extra-marital encounters, at least as far as the preliminaries were concerned, on the way to meet my husband in a city several hundred miles away. I was leisurely driving our convertible, top down, through some beautiful countryside when I noticed another car with a nice looking young man at the wheel obviously following me. When I passed a car, he would do likewise and then stay behind or pass me, only to drive along in front, keeping an eye on me through his rear-view mirror.

We had been playing this kind of highway-footsie for about fifty miles and it was getting me sexually more and more excited. So I decided I was going to stop at a roadside restaurant which was coming up, hoping that the fellow would take the hint. Of course, my scheme worked. As soon as I stopped, the young man pulled up alongside and asked to join me. Over our meal, he tactfully inquired how far I was going. I smiled and said, "Oh, a long ways. But I think I'll stop at the next town and look for a motel. I've just about had enough of driving for today. Besides, I don't want to drive at night." (This was stretching things a bit, because I wasn't all that tired, and it was obviously going to be light for another few hours!)

As it happened, the next place was his home town. "We'll be there in less than half an hour," he said. "Can I have a drink with you when we get there?"

"Sure," I replied, knowing that this was going to be it.

Again, we followed each other for the rest of the way.

When we got there, I checked in at a motel, and we went for a drink.

Afterward, we came back to the motel and made love.

But I must say that after we had finished, the fellow almost spoiled the whole thing. Once it was over, he started feeling guilty about his wife. He knew that she wouldn't like it or approve if she found out, and it was unlikely that she would believe the story he had told her over the telephone.

I was glad when he left, because I hate to listen to other people's wailings of guilt over their extra-marital sex. But he was so apologetic for having to leave me that I didn't have the heart to enlighten him about the fact that I had only been interested in having sex with him and not in establishing a deep friendship.

Brief encounters like this are exciting to me and add spice to my life, without having to get too involved socially or emotionally. I like, for instance, to go to conferences, meet a fellow, have a good time, go to bed with him, and then never see him again. I think the one thing one has to worry about in extra-marital affairs is that they don't become sticky or get out of control.

I've heard men complain that women expect too much once they go to bed with them, but this can work the other way 'round too. Most men just don't seem to believe that I might want to go to bed with them only once, but not a second time, or just a few times, but not forever.

They ask me, "What is the matter, don't you like me?" I tell them it has nothing to do with liking or not liking. I certainly liked them enough to have gone to bed with them in the first place. I try to explain to them that for me, part of the charm in extra-marital sex is doing it with different men. But they don't seem to believe it. If I go on and say that I have a steady sex partner in my husband whom I love, and that all I wanted was a casual sex relationship, they look at me as if I was committing a crime.

Another problem I have run into with extra-marital sex is that *the other fellow may insist that my husband must get jealous.* It's a hopeless task to try and convince this type of man that my husband is not jealous and that the guy doesn't have to worry about his coming after him with a gun.

I find this reaction on the part of some men hard to understand. I should think the other man would be relieved to know that everything is safe, because I don't like to think of another man's wife getting all steamed up and jealous over such a casual affair and perhaps even making trouble. It's unfortunate, but there it is, and it seems one can't avoid running into this sort of thing just as soon as one starts having any extra-marital sex at all.

Could I do without extra-marital affairs, if needs be? Certainly; I'm sure I would survive, but *I think sex would become more and more monotonous* to me. Extra-marital affairs seem to *keep me younger in spirit* and, I think, *make me a more affectionate person,* as well as a better sex partner: I know, *the more I love, the better a lover I become.* If that were not sufficient reason for my wanting to continue having extra-marital affairs when the right opportunities present themselves, I can only add that doing so has *enriched my marital sex life* as well.

As far as my husband's extra-marital affairs are concerned, I feel that they have the same good effect on his personality and on our marriage. His affairs do not threaten my inner security and I know that mine do not threaten his. We know too well what we have in each other's love.

Most significant to us is our informant's concern about *honesty* in the couple's marital relations; "I would never dream of having a secret affair." We think that decision was wise on the part of this couple. It probably was the one single factor which accounted the most for this marriage holding together under the inevitable strain to which any such unorthodox arrangement is bound to be subjected.

This kind of honesty in close interpersonal relations as in marriage, is perhaps more a matter of psychological common sense than of ethics in the traditional moralistic meaning of the term. Without such freedom of expression, communication suffers or breaks down entirely, and that always is the beginning of the end.

Partly as a consequence of this freedom of expression between the spouses and the mutual approval of their sexual behavior; partly because of the implied absence of conflicting ethical beliefs or religious precepts, our Sexual Sophisticate was not burdened by the usual sense of guilt attendant to socially disapproved conduct.

Our informant makes it clear that she did not wish to become too involved with other sex partners, but tried to keep her extra-marital relations casual. That this was not always appreciated by her men-friends strikes one as doubly ironic; usually, as she herself pointed out, it is the men who complain of being unable to get rid of women with whom they have had what they considered the most casual of relations. Here it was the exact opposite.

A discussion which we had with a famous French woman artist comes to mind in this connection. Sitting with her in her Paris studio one day, she told us over a cup of coffee how annoyed she was with some of the men with whom she had had sexual relations.

> You go to bed with them once and you cannot get rid of them. They keep calling you on the phone and pester you. Every one of them wants a deep friendship with you; it's maddening! To get away from that, I tried Negro men. I thought they would be more casual. *Pas de chance!* They were worse than the rest.

Apparently, not all women want above all a feeling of being loved, as is often assumed, at least not from every man that they may have sexual contact with.

Another psychological oddity consists of our Sexual Sophisticate's exasperation with some of her male friends who insisted that her husband should become *jealous*. We have often seen it to be the case that the extra-marital partner in similar situations is actively involved in erotically toned fantasies with the *other* spouse which have a distinctly homosexual or Oedipal cast.

More often than not, the lover of the married woman is himself not even aware of these fantasies, but seeks every opportunity to become involved with the other spouse. Sometimes this is accomplished with considerable risk to his own interests. It seems to us that many of the "adultery" dramas involving violence or other legal complications of which one reads in the daily press are motivated along these lines.

In the end, our Sexual Sophisticate frankly states that if for one reason or another she should be obliged to give up extra-marital contacts, it would not be a hardship to her. But she also felt that her sex life and her personality might suffer from such a restriction ("I think sex would become more and more monotonous to me").

If we now look back and compare the attitudes about extra-marital affairs of the four women from whose sex histories we have quoted, the emerging picture is a strange one: two of them, the More-Than-Average Housewife and the Doctor's Wife, wanted extra-marital contacts, but did not allow themselves to have them; the Married Lesbian did not really desire extra-marital affairs, but had had them; and the Sexual Sophisticate wanted extra-marital contacts and was having them.

In a society such as ours which places enormous emphasis on the importance of an individual's absorbing all of her (or his) sexual interests in an exclusive relationship with one partner, and one partner *only*, extra-marital relations are of necessity beset by innumerable and often serious problems. In spite of the ethical confusion of our age and the shifting of every moral value, extra-marital contacts are still publicly discussed in terms of "adultery." On the other hand, "adultery" is so widespread in Western society that serious social sanctions are only rarely enforced against the trespassers.

There seems to be no ready and sensible answer to the problems of extra-marital contacts within a social structure like ours. The matter is particularly touchy for the married woman who is economically dependent on her husband for support; and this, in our society, is still more often the case than not.

Things are not as easy for American or European wives desiring extra-marital affairs as is, for example, the case in a culture like Samoa. There, Margaret Mead tells us, a *woman's claim on her family's land*, "renders her as independent as her husband." In consequence, Professor Mead says, marriage in Samoa consists of "a very brittle monogamy, often trespassed and more often broken entirely and many adulteries occur . . . which hardly threaten the continuity of established relationships." On that South Sea Island, "romantic love as it occurs in our civilization, inextricably bound up with ideas of monogamy, exclusiveness, jealousy and undeviating fidelity does not occur . . ." So far, so good. But the inevitable hitch comes when we hear that among the islanders, ". . . passionate attachment to one person which lasts for a long period and persists in the face of discouragement but does not bar other relationships, is rare . . ."

In other words, the anthropological material suggests that with a different type of economic structure and a more relaxed attitude toward monogamy, one may have to be satisfied with less intense relationships between the spouses, more fluidity (and therefore possibly more insecurity) in the family situation, and a loss of what we mean to include under the catch-all heading of romantic love.

It looks therefore as if in the matter of monogamy and

extra-marital relations we could not have our cake and eat it too: at least that would definitely be the impression, if it were not for the occasional testimonies of individuals like our Sexual Sophisticate, suggesting still another and possibly more satisfactory solutions.

Whether they are right and are showing us a better way, another generation than ours will have to decide. But in the face of the glaring failure of conventional monogamous marriage as we know it, one can only hope that it should be so.

X

The Ways of Love

WE have mentioned what might be one possible solution for a few couples to the rising divorce figures, a solution, however, which is based on the premise of a *happy* married relationship maintained and augmented by a liberal point of view. But the basic difficulty with many marriages, if not most, is that of sexually *dissatisfied* partners. A large part of this frustration, for both men and women, stems from the sexual taboos which have been created for women and adopted by them.

It is as necessary for women to learn more about their real sexual potentiality, as it is for men to learn how to help them develop this potentiality, for while it may be true that the ability to bring a woman to orgasm is not the total solution, it is equally true that without this ability few marriages can succeed. Let us therefore examine some of the reasons why so many Western women appear to be frigid, or semi-frigid, and, by reference to our main informants, why this does not need to be so.

Judging from experience in our own culture only, one might also expect the woman elsewhere in the world to be universally the more passive partner in sexual relations. This impression would be further reinforced by the accounts of male travelers to Asia and other parts of the world who return home, complaining that the women in these exotic cultures are still more passive than is generally the case in our own society.

The facts of the matter are, however, quite different from the appearance. True, some other societies similar to our own have a tradition by which women are expected and encouraged to remain more or less passive during sexual relations and, above all, not to make the initial approach.

However, there are societies which, unlike our own, allow and expect their women to play a more active and aggressive role. In such cultures the women are anything but passive in the sex act or reticent in their approach. What seems to make the difference between one type of society and the other is how much freedom for sexual play is allowed in *adolescence* and *pre-adolescence*. Wherever society is strict in these respects and where modesty and submissiveness are considered feminine virtues, women are generally incapable of and unwilling to take the initiative and play an active, aggressive role in sexual relations. In these societies, the percentage of anorgastic women is high, no matter whether they happen to inhabit a tropic island or a Western suburb.

But if a society allows its adolescent and preadolescent girls more freedom—as, for instance, in Samoa or among the Muria of Central India—they grow up to be sexually fully as active and aggressive as the men. In these societies, women expect and are expected to experience orgasm more or less regularly in their sexual activities.

It is not surprising that in these more permissive societies which breed the active, sexually aggressive type of woman, she is more likely to leave visible marks of affection on her partner. Many a South Sea islander emerges from an amorous encounter in the bush with scratch and bite marks all over his body and is teased by the villagers for having encountered a tiger on his way.

Some women in our own society are also known to engage in intentional biting or scratching either during foreplay or, more frequently, at the time of orgasm.

The poet Heinrich Heine has used this frequent practice of women during their love play as the subject matter of one of the verses in his poem "On Hasting's Battlefield":

> *And on his shoulders she beheld three scars,*
> *And kissed them once again: wounds of no wars,*
> *No foreman's brand had smitten—*
> *Three little scars her own white teeth had bitten.*

As said, travelers often return deeply disappointed from visits to cultures which are otherwise known for their passionate, sexually active, and highly orgastic women. There are, however, good reasons for this at first puzzling contradiction. Anthropologist Malinowski, who spent half a lifetime studying the life and customs of the Melanesians, suggested that if the sexual experiences of white men with native women are disappointing, the disappointment seems to be mutual and the fault to lie mostly with the white man. Says Dr. Malinowski:

> . . . Above all, the natives despise the European position and consider it unpractical and improper . . . As they say: "the man overlies heavily the woman; he presses her heavily downwards, she cannot respond."
>
> Altogether the natives are certain that white men do not know how to carry out intercourse effectively. As a matter of fact, it is one of the special accomplishments of native cookboys and servants who have been for some time in the employ of white traders, planters, or officials, to imitate the copulatory methods of their masters, . . . Gomaya's performance consisted in the imitation of a very clumsy reclining position, and in the execution of a few sketchy and flabby movements. In this the *brevity* and *lack of vigor* of the European performance was caricatured. Indeed, *to the native idea, the white man achieves orgasm far too quickly;* and there seems to be no doubt that the Melanesian takes a much longer time and employs a much greater amount of mechanical energy to reach the same result. *This, together with the handicap of the unfamiliar position, probably accounts for the complaints of*

white men that native girls are not responsive. Many a white informant has spoken to me about perhaps the only word in the native language which he ever learned, kubilabala ("move on horizontally"), repeated to him with some intensity during the sexual act. This verb defines the horizontal motion during sexual intercourse which should be *mutual.*

In our interviewing it has been the almost constant complaint of women (especially in America and Great Britain) that their male partners were either *too fast, clumsy, or too limited in their sexual technique.* On the other hand, most of the women who complained thus did not see it as their role to initiate the desired changes themselves, or else felt unable to do so.

There is nothing gained by placing the blame for this failure in love techniques, more the rule than the exception in Western society, either on the women or on the men. Van de Velde has devoted a whole book to the purpose of teaching women "sex efficiency through exercise." He describes and illustrates certain gymnastics, designed to strengthen and limber up the abdominal and pelvic muscles. How the men are supposed to keep up with such "sex-efficient" females, he did not say.

Balzac, on the other hand, was more inclined to blame his own sex for sexual inefficiency. Most men, he used to say, are about as adroit in making love as an orangutan in playing the piano. He also said: "If a man cannot on two successive nights, afford distinct and different pleasures to the woman he has made his wife, she has married too soon."

Primitive societies have always recognized the need for imparting to their young the necessary physical skills required for the most strenuous and artful types of intercourse which they favor. For that purpose they have ingeniously devised a number of erotic dances, connected with their puberty rites, which teach adolescent boys and girls *by pantomime* the motions and rhythms of various intercourse techniques.

A comparable tradition is not only absent, but utterly unthinkable in the West, at least as far as the teaching of young people is concerned, unless one wants to go back to Antiquity for a different approach to sexuality and erotic finesse. However, there has more recently been a revival of interest in the refinements of sexual relations and sex techniques to which the flood of sex instruction literature and the so-called "marriage manuals" bear eloquent witness.

Drs. Abraham and Hannah Stone have put it this way in their previously quoted marriage manual: "It is only in the last few centuries that the *art of sex* has been largely neglected and even suppressed. Now we are once again realizing the importance of an understanding approach in sexual love, and are placing greater emphasis upon an adequate and varied technique in the marital sex relation." (Italics ours.)

What Western society has been slowest in recognizing is the importance of an *erotic atmosphere* for more satisfactory sex relations. The pressure of time and the economic stress under which most of us live and labor make the cultivation of such an atmosphere, of course, considerably more difficult than, say, for the French *élite* of the eighteenth century among whom eroticism, albeit of a rather moribund sort, did indeed flourish. Yet, our Sexual Sophisticate may have a point when, in an off-record aside to us, she suggested, "If men would spend less time in the bar and more time in the bedroom, they might become better lovers."

Likewise, the example of some of our informants, e.g. that of the Doctor's Wife and—oddly enough—also of the Married Lesbian, which we shall discuss in a different context, as well as that of the More-Than-Average Housewife, shows that even busy modern couples can, if they are really interested, create quite an erotic atmosphere in their own home.

We shall here only quote the More-Than-Average Housewife who remarked as follows to this point:

Whether we want to have sex depends on a lot of things such as outside stimulation. Most of the time it's mutual. A look, word, or touch is a signal, or maybe we just feel it. We usually let the other know several hours ahead, so we can get the kids off to school or to a show. We shower, brush teeth. . . . Sometimes I put on perfume, and we have a highball or two, if we don't have to work afterwards. If it's at night, after the kids are asleep, we usually have a soft light, as it stimulates us to see each other. When my husband's home in the daytime, it is an exciting change to have it at noon while the kids are at school and then take a nap.

To some, the preparations of our informant may seem exaggerated and to be robbing their sex life of spontaneity. The Doctor's Wife, for instance, placed so much emphasis on spontaneity that she felt even the previous insertion of the diaphragm to be too much premeditation, and this seems to apply to many other women. However, she too spoke of putting on sexually exciting clothes and high-heeled shoes before intercourse to cultivate a more conducive atmosphere in which a certain kind of sex talk between her and her husband played a major role.

The More-Than-Average Housewife also mentions that the couple use a *soft light* in preparation for intercourse and during it, and stressed the importance of *seeing* each other during all phases of their sexual relations. She leaves no doubt that being able to watch each other during intercourse had as much significance for her as for her husband, though it is generally assumed that women are less interested in these visual stimuli than men (compare also the similar remarks of our other informants elsewhere in this book emphasizing the value of visual stimuli).

There are nowadays many less women who insist on total darkness during sexual relations than was commonly the case only a generation ago; another indication that "typically feminine shyness" is a *learned* response rather than a biological fact.

Continuing with the More-Than-Average Housewife, she goes on to tell of the couple's technique during foreplay:

> When we are ready for bed, he is erect in a couple of minutes, usually to my touch. I love to french-kiss; he doesn't until aroused. He usually kisses me mostly on my breasts. I believe this stimulates me more than anything. I definitely like it. *I'm usually touching him all over*, especially his penis. I go up and down on his body and he on mine. His fingers are on my clitoris and in and out, five, ten or fifteen minutes.
>
> By now I am aroused and have had enough of the foreplay. I might perform fellatio on him and I might not. If he's been without sex longer than a few days, I usually don't because if I stimulate him too much, he can't hold his erection as long as I would like him to. Maybe we lie 69 and he plays with me manually, massaging my clitoris. He also likes to see and feel my breasts rubbing against his penis. Anyway by then I'm as ready as I'll ever be and so eager. In fact I usually want to get on top of him right away, but he holds me back, and I like it.

In these two short paragraphs, our More-Than-Average Housewife mentions a number of stimulation techniques which are highly effective during the woman's excitement phase. Her emphasis on *touch* is as much *active as passive;* she likes to touch her husband's body, including his genitals, and be touched by him.

Our informant mentions touching her husband's penis with her breasts, but it seems that this is done mostly for his benefit, though the sight of his arousal and the side-effect of breast stimulation must be experienced as pleasant by her as well.

Most importantly, the woman describes that her *husband manually stimulates her clitoris, labia and vaginal outlet* for periods of *five to fifteen* minutes, which is indeed more than average for most couples. This type of stimulation is apparently continued by the husband until she gives clear indications that she is ready for coitus to begin.

There is apparently also some kind of teasing technique involved in this couple's foreplay in that the husband may at first prevent the wife from getting into position for vaginal intercourse, a gesture which seems to excite our informant. The only thing which this husband will not do during foreplay or at any time is to stimulate his wife's genitals orally, as pointed out elsewhere.

We shall now consider what the More-Than-Average Housewife has to tell us about her difficulties with all coital positions, except one:

> I feel every time that if I'm going to get this orgasm, I've got to start working. I put my feet under his buttocks and my knees straight out to the side (why in the hell do I have to depend for my happiness on the most uncomfortable position that exists?). I lean over on my hands and move towards him and back. The more *pressure* I get, the better. I think he puts his hands back of my hips, at the same time raising his own hips. We do this for about five minutes, I believe, but am not sure, because at this stage I'm busy and maybe already only half-aware of what's going on. I'm getting more and more excited. He usually nibbles my breasts or kisses me. Now this might take another ten minutes or so. If it takes much longer, my feet or knees might cramp, but usually I reach orgasm about this time.

In the following section our informant attempts to explain why only the one position which she described is able to bring her to orgasm and how all other positions she had tried had failed:

> *I need a great deal of pressure and friction* between the penis and myself. I press against him with my whole weight in my hips which includes his hand pressure on my hips. I can't get that pressure in any other position. I can't get it by manual stimulation, and if he's on top of me, I don't get sufficient pressure even on the floor. If we are on our sides with his front to my back, it is like nothing to me, except for the foreplay. The side position with both of us facing each other is

even worse. I've tried all the positions, even to practically standing on my head. He has had me standing on every size footstool, chair, pillows, beds, and sitting on his lap. He kills himself trying, but still there is only that one position in which I can reach Cloud 9.

There seems nothing wrong or unusual about this woman's decided preference for the position which she favors. It is preferred by many women, gives the woman a high degree of freedom of movement, and affords good contact between penis and clitoris, if the woman is leaning forward. She therefore seems to be magnifying her difficulties somewhat, especially when one realizes that she is able to enjoy other positions and stimulation techniques during various stages of intercourse and has to rely solely on the particular position described by her during parts of the plateau and orgasmic phases.

At the time when our informant was writing her sex history, her husband was at home, recovering from an abdominal operation, and she was getting quite frustrated. Her problem was that manual stimulation was insufficient to bring her to orgasm and that her husband, who refused oral contact, had, since the operation, been unable to engage in coitus.

It was at this point that our More-Than-Average Housewife playfully threatened her husband that if matters continued in this fashion much longer, she would have to look for somebody else to find out what cunnilingus might do for her.

With this as the background, we understand when she says,

. . . My threat of cunnilingus must have paid off partially, as it got us making love in my favorite position tonight. He had been babying his incision, but I was careful not to lie on his tummy. He's had the incision for sixteen days and I've been without sex for twenty-six days. Well, anyway, he stimulated me manually while I performed fellatio on him. He really played with me almost to the point of orgasm. Then I begged him to let me mount (after we had tried the rear-entry position for a while). I promised not to lean on him too hard.

He pushed back of my hips and I pushed forward and back and went into my dream-world orgasm. It was almost as good as usual, but I held it down to four orgasms, because I didn't want to hurt him or tire him. Then I stayed on a while longer to rest. Finally I got off and got down between his legs and masturbated him by hand, as he can't get on me yet with his incision. Then I lay on his legs to rest. Actually I'd rather have had him have his orgasm in me so that I could have had another orgasm. However, I know that if I masturbated him, he'll want it sooner again. I notice he needs sex sooner after I have satisfied him manually or performed fellatio on him than if he has complete intercourse.

He's so listless and discouraged from his operation that there is a method in my madness. I'll soon get his mind on sex again. I think intercourse will help him to relax and recover sooner. Nothing else interests him much at this point anyway.

I feel a quiet peace now. I think I'll go to bed. I've tucked him in and bent over and whispered, "Thanks, darling." He whispered, "It was all in a good cause"—smart man, smart man.

It is difficult to understand why our More-Than-Average Housewife did not allow her husband to bring her to orgasm manually when, according to her own statement, she was almost at the point of orgasm. This might be the appropriate starting point for any psychological investigation into her problem of supposedly being able to achieve orgasm in only the one position.

In the light of these factors, one cannot help but wonder how serious she really was about her desire to have someone perform cunnilingus on her. Or, if she had the opportunity to experience this form of stimulation, would she *allow herself* to come to orgasm in this manner any more than she did through manual stimulation?

However, our informant's idea of distracting her husband (who was apparently suffering from a mild post-operative depression) through sexual intercourse was perhaps sounder than she herself might have suspected. Considerable testimony from both men and women, borne out by some specific evidence, indicates the beneficial effect of successful sexual experience on the emotional and physical state of the individual.

Normally, when her husband was in good health, our More-Than-Average Housewife's sex routine was quite different. If he had been without sex for some time, for instance if he had been away from home for a week or more, she would first make sure that he was not going to frustrate her by having his orgasm too soon:

> If he's been without sex for some time, I'll satisfy him first quick-like by hand and wait a few hours or even a whole day until I come to him for myself. I do this, because he naturally can't hold his erection as long as usual when he's too hungry for sex.

Then, during intercourse, she would first mount her husband until she had had a number of orgasms in that manner, after which she would engage in other positions which were apparently preferred by him:

> I figure, now he's due for his turn . . . I lie down beside him. Usually he's still erect. I fondle his penis a little, or if he's eager, I get on my stomach and lift my hips . . . If he doesn't have his orgasm too quick, we have it together again that way. But rarely is it as good an orgasm for me as the first ones, though almost as good. . . .
> He prefers this back position to all others. I wish I could get right into orgasm this way, but I can't, until I've been mounting him a while. . . .

Our informant's sex technique was, as we see, dependent on her ability to experience *multiple* orgasm.

The passage also points out a contradiction of sorts: our informant had said that the position in which she was mounting her husband was the only one which was able to bring her to orgasm. In this passage, however, she seems to indicate that she is able to achieve orgasm in other positions too—provided she has already experienced one or more orgasms before. (Compare also the statement of the Sexual Sophisticate about the greater ease of achieving orgasm under similar conditions, in "The Struggle for Orgasm.")

In the next passage, our More-Than-Average Housewife mentions her experiences with the legs-on-the-man's-shoulders position and the significance of penis size for her.

Referring at times to her pre-marital experiences, she says,

> We tried every position (except with me mounted). Once I was on my back and he was on his hands and knees, and he put my legs on his shoulders. I recall it was out of this world, but it hurt too. While my husband and I do it that way now sometimes, it's even more exhausting than with me mounted. It seems to me that if a man could thrust throughout the sex act as long and hard as his last two or three thrusts just before he ejaculates, I could come to orgasm sooner. It also seems as if I can feel his penis more before his climax because it seems as if he swells lightly just then. I know I also had it as good with the boxer who had such a big penis. He gave it to me, but good, in the same position. Whereas the guy who couldn't produce, was much smaller even when erect, and never helped me.
>
> I don't give a damn what all the experts say, for me size does make a difference. I want one medium or large, or nothing. Maybe I'm just a phallus worshipper, but, the bigger the better, that's the way I feel. At present I have between medium and large, but I think I'll go into further research to prove my point. And, of course, a man's physical stature has nothing to do with it. That awfully passionate soldier was stocky, not much taller than I am, and he had about the biggest I've ever seen.

But no matter how long her husband held out or how many orgasms she'd had, our More-Than-Average House-wife usually felt that she could have gone on for still more:

When he withdraws I hate it, because sometimes I feel like I could come some more. Here is where I could use a second hard husband around the house!

If a statement like this seems shocking, it is only because every truth, when frankly expressed, comes first as a sort of shock. Yet, what our informant is stating, is nothing but what scores of other women also feel, but do not dare to express, or even tell themselves. Far from considering our More-Than-Average Housewife therefore as a sort of over-sexed nymphomaniac, we would consider the strength of her sex drive and of the millions of women like her, as perfectly normal, in fact as what ought to be the rule rather than the exception, if it were not for the social inhibitions to which most people, and particularly women, have traditionally been subject in our culture.

THE SEXUAL SOPHISTICATE

Turning from the More-Than-Average Housewife to the Sexual Sophisticate, we find that she also rates the on-top position highly among her favorite sex techniques, but not as exclusively as the former. With dispassionate objectivity but keen personal interest she lists the advantages and disadvantages which various positions and intercourse techniques hold for her:

The positions which I like best are the ones that leave me *freedom of movement.* If I am pinned down in any position, I find it almost impossible to become part of the whole act. Participation in sex, to me, means some degree of movement. This is no doubt partly due to the fact that the *rhythm* of intercourse is one of the aspects of love-making that is very important to me.

I find the *sitting position,* in which the woman is sitting on top of the man, one of the *least tiring* and, besides, it allows the woman to be *free to move.* She has the support of her feet and the man can help to lift her up and down by putting his hands under her buttocks. My only regret is that most of today's chairs or beds are unfortunately not ideally suited for this position.

I enjoy the *man on top* of me only if he supports his weight so that I am not immobilized. The only exception is when we are lying together and not moving very much. *After orgasm*, however, I like to feel the weight of my partner's body on mine.

At times I enjoy the *side position*, although this position makes it more difficult for both partners to be vigorously active. I think it is ideal when one wants to have a prolonged episode with gentle movements.

Another favorite position of mine is *squatting on top of the man* which seems to allow for the best co-ordinating movements between the two partners. An additional advantage lies in the fact that in this position either one can use his hands to stimulate the clitoris.

I also very much enjoy it, if the man is lying on top of me with his legs falling outside of my legs which are pressed close together. The penis is then tightly clasped between the labia which are pressed together by my legs. It takes very little and only gentle movements to create voluptuous feelings that way. This position is ideal if one has already had one orgasm, because the genitals are then hypersensitive to the slightest movements and pressures.

As far as the *standing* position is concerned, I am convinced this is satisfactory only to the Yogis, because I have never been able to accomplish this with any degree of grace and relaxation.

A few years ago when visiting Paris I was invited to see a sexual exhibition. The three women and one man were superb performers and seemed to be enjoying it as much as the audience. There was especially one technique they used which looked promising. They called it the scissor position in which the man and the woman can either lie down or partially sit. Lying down on their backs, their heads are at opposite ends with the woman's right leg over the top of the man's abdomen, while her left leg is under his right leg, or vice versa. The genitals are in apposition to each other. If the couple wish to partially sit, they can keep in balance by grasping each other's opposite forearms. Like in a square dance the woman grasps with her right hand her partner's right hand as they face each other.

I had read about this position before, but for some reason had never attempted it. Watching the couple perform in this fashion, it became obvious to me that it had many advantages. I have subsequently tried it and found it a most enjoyable variation.

The other day, I heard a man say people look ridiculous during intercourse. I recalled having heard this said before, and yet the man's statement had a bit of a shock effect on me. How could anyone feel that way and still enjoy his sex life?

I had seldom felt that way myself. Still, I had to admit that there had been some occasions, fortunately only a few of them, on which I too had felt somewhat ridiculous during the sex act. They had been primarily situations in which I had not felt sufficiently stimulated, but had mainly obliged my partner, or when I had been asked to assume a position which I did not find sexually exciting.

One of these, to me, rather unsatisfactory positions, is the one in which the woman kneels leaning forward, with the man approaching from behind. The other is the one in which the woman lies on her back, with her legs resting on the man's shoulders.

In each of these two positions I have found myself ridiculously and bizarrely immobilized and not been able to derive much pleasure from them. On the contrary, with my legs on the man's shoulders, I have often felt actual pain instead of pleasure.

I must confess that kneeling dog-fashion on my hands and knees during intercourse has, at times, made me feel humiliated. Not only because this position seems more animalistic than any other to the woman as she crouches on all fours, but also because it makes the woman a more or less passive object, instead of an equal participant in the act. Either one must remain stationary like the female in heat, or if one attempts to move, one can only move into something one cannot see.

In addition to all this, I have sometimes been afraid to assume this position, because the man may take advantage of it by attempting anal intercourse. On the other hand—and I realize this is contradictory but nevertheless it is true—I do occasionally like and desire sex in the kneeling position, maybe just *because* one is made to feel so animalistic in it. Like no other, the rear-entry position gives one the sensation of the man's penis literally pounding the vagina with its deep thrusts, a feeling which can be highly pleasurable.

It just occurs to me that during masturbation I sometimes imagine myself kneeling in precisely this rear-entry position about which I have otherwise so many reservations. At those times, I have the fantasy of spurring on my partner, shouting "Harder, harder!" and "deeper!"

We see that the Sexual Sophisticate emphasizes *freedom of movement, variety,* and *rhythm,* whereas the More-Than-Average Housewife emphasized the importance for her of *friction, pressure, vigorous* and *prolonged* coitus, and last, but not least, *penis size.* The Sexual Sophisticate did not mention penis size in this context, but elsewhere said that penis size did not matter much to her, except that she disliked overly small or overly large male genitals.

Comparisons between the reactions of these two women are especially useful in that they highlight certain similarities as well as striking differences in their psychological sex response. What they teach us, above all, is *respect for individual differences* in appraising people's sexual preferences. But they also show that in spite of the tremendous spread in the variety of women's individual response patterns, one can clearly discern the *same underlying physiological reactions* to sexual stimulation which are characteristic of the various phases of the woman's total response cycle.

It would be repetitious to add to the descriptions of individual reactions to sex techniques from the histories of other women informants. However, a word about women's reactions during the last, or *resolution* phase seems in place.

THE MORE-THAN-AVERAGE HOUSEWIFE

Our More-Than-Average Housewife tells us about that aspect of her sexual experience:

This I know; no matter whether I feel completely satisfied, or only partly, I can't drop off to sleep instantly; I'm too stimulated. I might be restless, my leg muscles may be hurting (aching), and then sometime later peace comes over me. I know, I am the restless type, but sometimes I definitely feel a great peace around me some time after intercourse. Maybe it lasts twelve or twenty-four hours.

The fact that this woman's sexual excitement subsides at times only very slowly even after one or more satisfactory orgasms, is also probably due to her potential for experiencing at least five to ten orgasms in succession. It is therefore quite possible that such a woman is left in a relative degree of sexual tension even after orgasmic experiences which would result in the complete physical and psychic exhaustion of many other women.

The Female Psychoanalyst also commented that she experienced only one orgasm at a time and felt that this was fully sufficient. She implied that any more would be too much for her. In those cases one would be justified in expecting the post-orgasmic sexual tension to be less and the resolution phase to be proportionately shorter, and this seems to be substantiated by the results of our interviews.

THE SEXUAL SOPHISTICATE

The Sexual Sophisticate occupied in these respects a middle ground; she stated that she usually enjoys an excitement phase of medium length and prefers to experience multiple orgasm. But her remarks also indicate that generally she experiences a feeling of well-being and relaxation after satisfactory sexual intercourse:

How one feels after sex depends naturally on several factors. I shall attempt to describe what I generally feel without discussing the exceptions. *If I have sex during the day*, I frequently find that after orgasm *I am relaxed, refreshed and*

more energetic. On the other hand, if I have it *in the evening,
I am just content to go to sleep.*

I do not like to have sex when I am overly tired as I think
it becomes an ordeal that makes one still more exhausted. But
I have observed that at times when I am tired (not overly
tired) my tiredness disappears during foreplay and that even
after the orgasm I feel better than I did before.

I have found that orgasm *can be the best remedy for minor
physical ailments and psychological upsets!* Although one
hesitates to begin having sex when one does not feel well, for
instance, when one has a headache, slight cold, etc., the final
results can well be worth it. Quite often I have simply found
myself after a happy sexual experience completely relaxed and
the tension gone which had been causing the headache or other
complaints.

I have noticed that sinus troubles or nasal congestions may
clear up suddenly after orgasm.

I rarely enjoy the "quickie" which some men seem to like.
To me, sex is at its best if I can take my time and enjoy the
closeness of my partner before and afterwards. I like to have
the man stay inside after orgasm so that I can feel the little
spasms and gradual shrinking of the penis.

Strange as it may sound, I like to feel the weight of the
man's body on me after orgasm when it is no longer inhibiting
my movements. Frequently, if I have been on top during
intercourse, I like to roll over after orgasm together with my
partner so that I can have this pleasant sensation. It amazes
me how light the human body feels at these times; almost
weightless. But, as I have previously said, if the man is lying
on top of me before orgasm, then I feel and resent his weight
as much as if it were a stone.

The Latin philosopher who said *Post coitum animal triste*
(After coitus the animal is sad) must not have been thinking
of the human female! This at least is clear from virtually all
the sex histories of the women whom we interviewed and
who more or less regularly experienced orgasm in their sexual
relations.

Few, however, have gone so far as to credit orgasm with
remedial qualities against headaches, colds, emotional troubles,
and so forth, as our Sexual Sophisticate has done. Still, we see

no reason why orgasmic tension release should not have a positive effect on the person's sense of general well-being and induce a feeling of emotional as well as physical intactness. If these effects do not always dominate the post-orgasmic picture it is due to the equally relevant fact that the physical and psychic effort involved in the build-up and release of sexual tension can be considerable. If such an experience takes place at the end of the day or when the individual is already fatigued for other reasons, the post-orgasmic relaxation may simply lead, as our informant described, to the restoration of energy through sleep.

As we consider in retrospect the statements of the quoted informants, one can see one common denominator: the significance of adequate stimulation techniques in *all* phases of sexual intercourse.

Effective stimulation techniques are perhaps especially crucial during the first or excitement phase. It is not that the woman's build-up of sexual tension necessarily proceeds more slowly than that of the man, but, as we have already said and wish to emphasize, *the greater the degree of sexual arousal during the excitement phase, the better the chances are for a woman to experience an intense orgasmic phase and to experience multiple orgasm.*

It is probably no accident that female anthropologists have stressed the significance of effective stimulation techniques during foreplay by making comparisons with other cultures. Says Margaret Mead:

> . . . Societies like Samoa that emphasize a *highly varied* and *diffuse type of foreplay* will include in the repertoire of the male acts that will effectively awaken *almost all* women, however differently constituted they may be. But in cultures in which many forms of foreplay are forbidden, or simply ruled out by social arrangements that insist on both partners being *clothed,* or on the *absence of lights,* or on the *muffling of all body odors* by scented deodorants, *this potentiality, which all women can develop* under sufficiently favorable circumstances,

may be ignored for a large proportion or for almost all of them. (Italics ours.)

Put into the terms of our discussion, what Margaret Mead seems to be suggesting is that the rest of the woman's sex response during the later phases of intercourse depends largely on what happens during foreplay, or technically the excitement phase. One cannot agree more wholeheartedly. But our informants have taught us that the necessary postscript to this emphasis is that *effective stimulation* has to be carried through the plateau and orgasmic phases as well, if the experience is to be successful for the woman.

It is at this point that many of the intercourse techniques which are popular in the Western world falter and rob a large percentage of women of the *orgasmic potential* which, as Margaret Mead so boldly states, "all women can develop."

As to the last or resolution phase of the woman's sex response, we wish to stress the need for *leisure* which our Sexual Sophisticate indicated as an essential element to her complete satisfaction. If, as the Doctor's Wife said, "there is nothing worse than to be flopped on your back and jumped upon when you're still cold," there is also, as many women have assured us, nothing more chilling than to have sexual relations abruptly terminated immediately after the climax.

One might even go as far as to say that the last or "resolution" phase of the woman's sex response has been almost as much neglected in the Western world as the initial stages of love-making. It would however be a mistake to interpret the desire on the part of many women for physical contact with their partner after a satisfactory (and *only* after a *satisfactory* experience), as an indication of female sentimentality or even as a special female "need to be loved," as is often assumed to be the case.

What it does show rather, is that the genital and general body contact with her partner after intercourse can afford the woman perhaps even greater pleasure than is possible for the man. Of course, the man's continued interest in her during the resolution phase may also represent to the woman a sign of human respect on the part of the man for his female partner as well as another proof of his consideration to give her the fullest measure of physical and psychic pleasure possible. But then, the same also applies to the man of any erotic refinement and emotional sensitivity.

XI

Women and Oral Sex

In order to understand the attitudes of American and English women (as well as men) toward mouth-genital contacts, one must see the whole problem against the background of the pillory and the stocks. Strangely enough, in conservative England, in whose mores these repressive attitudes, no doubt, originated, mouth-genital contacts as such are not punishable. Still more strangely, supposedly forward-looking America still has certain medieval laws on the statute books of most states, providing heavy fines and long imprisonment for both cunnilingus and fellatio.

In general, the laws against mouth-genital contacts are not enforced. And if they are occasionally applied, it is usually no more than a form of legal harassment, disguised persecution, or personal grudge. Still, even at this writing, there are some individuals serving out long prison sentences who have been convicted and sentenced under these incredibly inhuman and outdated sex laws.

As for the rest of the world's attitudes toward mouth-genital contacts, the French are probably the most permissive European nation in this respect, though Sweden and Denmark seem to rank close seconds. Among primitive cultures, there are some six other societies (mainly in Oceania) in which oral stimulation is widely practiced. Ponapean men, for instance, use both their tongue and teeth on the woman's labia. Other societies like the Alorese seem to be as schizoid and conflicted about cunnilingus and fellatio as our own culture. In that group oral sex techniques (especially cunnilingus) are widely practiced, but not really approved.

We know from the Kinsey studies that more than half of all the couples in his sample were at times practicing mouth-genital sex techniques. But this still tells us relatively little about the attitudes of those who practice them.

According to Kinsey, more men prefer to perform cunnilingus than women want to perform fellatio. This was in keeping with observations on animals in which the male usually outdoes the female in these respects. While all this is most likely true, one must not forget that there still exists a *substantial minority of men* who like to have their female partners perform fellatio on them, while they themselves remain unwilling or reluctant to engage in mouth-genital contacts.

THE MORE-THAN-AVERAGE HOUSEWIFE

A typical example in point would be our More-Than-Average Housewife and her husband. In her case, the husband showed much resistance against performing cunnilingus while she had managed to overcome her own initial prejudice toward fellatio.

Said our informant:

After we'd been married for a while, I started to perform fellatio on my husband. But he would not do it to me, and I doubt whether he ever will. I don't believe even now I could perform fellatio on any other man. I didn't want to do it at first even to him. But I loved him and knew he wanted it and it had its advantages.

I don't think it particularly arouses me. Certainly not as much as hand play does. That is partly why I don't think I could ever become a lesbian. Anyway, my husband seems reluctant to perform cunnilingus on me, and I don't urge it. His manual stimulation helps, but he can't seem to bring me to orgasm that way. Neither can I by masturbation. Both just warm me more and make me eager for intercourse. That's why I think that even if he did perform cunnilingus on me, it wouldn't be any more effective than just the manual stimulation.

Leaving aside for the moment the husband's reaction, we find the wife arguing both for and against cunnilingus. She wants it, yet she is doubtful whether it would bring her to orgasm any more than manual stimulation has done for her in the past. Elsewhere in her sex history she is more definite in her desire to have cunnilingus performed on her:

> I asked my husband: "Why don't you want to perform cunnilingus on me?" He said, "I don't think it would do you any good." I said, "But how do you know?" He replied, "Well, I don't think you've got a clitoris." I said, "How do we know, if you don't want to try? And why haven't you done it for the other girls you knew who had a clitoris?" I also told him that Frank Harris says it's wonderful. But he said he won't. I told him, "If you won't do it, I'm going to find someone to perform cunnilingus on me so I'll find out what it's really like before I die."

Why are so many men unwilling to perform cunnilingus on women?

In the example we have just heard, the husband's objections were obviously not much more than thinly disguised rationalizations for a deeper aversion to cunnilingus.

Negative feelings about cunnilingus are perfectly understandable from a psychological point of view considering cultural attitudes about such matters. After all, Western sphincter morality has succeeded in deeply engraining in all of us a powerful aversion not only to the human waste products but also to anything associated with bodily secretions and odors.

Women are keenly aware of this and for that reason sometimes refuse to have cunnilingus performed on them, even if the man offers to do so. A woman first wants to be absolutely sure that the man does not think less of her for having allowed him to do it and that he is not just forcing himself out of a mistaken sense of duty or obligation to please the woman.

THE SEXUAL SOPHISTICATE

This anxiety on the part of some women is well expressed in the following statement by our Sexual Sophisticate:

> The first time a man performed cunnilingus on me I felt embarrassed and ashamed. It seemed so animalistic and forbidden. I was afraid he would be revolted by such close contact with my genitals; after all, they do have some odor and taste, even though one may have just showered. For this reason, I found it difficult to relax and felt that any hesitation which my partner showed meant that he really didn't want to do it, but was forcing himself for my benefit, a thought which made me feel even worse. (It is hard to accept at first that there is any pleasure for the person performing cunnilingus!) Later, when I learned to relax, it became a marvelous feeling to just lie back and let someone give me so much pleasure.

While worries about the man's reactions to cunnilingus are very frequent with women, we have occasionally heard others speak of less common fears connected with this technique. One woman told us, for instance, that her husband was so impetuous and "avaricious" when performing cunnilingus that she felt as though she was being "devoured" by him.

There was, however, general agreement among the vast majority of the group of women interviewed by us who had had such experiences that mouth-genital stimulation was highly effective both in foreplay or as a means of bringing them to orgasm. These impressions are confirmed by the findings of the Kinsey group and the most recent biological research on the woman's sex response. In both of these cases, the overriding significance of the *clitoris* as woman's primary sexual target organ has been firmly established and the significance of clitoral stimulation techniques confirmed from every point of view. The authors of some of the better marriage manuals recognized this fact from their own vast clinical experience long before the latest confirming scientific evidence, and had advised their readers accordingly.

Abraham and Hannah Stone, for example, said in their widely known marriage manual which is still recognized as one of the best in the field:

> Because of the concentration of the sensual impulses around the area of the clitoris, *many women, although unable to reach an orgasm from intercourse, can do so with comparative ease if the clitoral region is stimulated directly.* (Italics ours.)

And, with a broad hint toward cunnilingus, the same authors added:

> There is nothing perverse or degrading . . . in any sex practice which is undertaken for the purpose of promoting a more harmonious sexual adjustment between a husband and wife in marriage.

Of the older marriage manuals, Van de Velde said the following about cunnilingus in his now classical manual, *Ideal Marriage*:

> This type of stimulation has many advantages. First of all the lack of local secretions ceases to be a drawback, and even becomes an advantage. Secondly, the *acuteness of the pleasure* it excites and the variety of tactile sensation it provides will ensure that the previous deficiency is made good.

And elsewhere in the same book:

> The *genital kiss is particularly calculated to overcome frigidity and fear* in hitherto inexperienced women who have had no erotic practice, and are as yet hardly capable of specific sexual desire.

Van de Velde also stresses the physiological advantages of cunnilingus in that it provides for continued natural lubrication even under prolonged stimulation:

> But the most simple and obvious substitute for the inadequate lubricant is the natural moisture of the salivary glands. It is always available, though it has, of course, the disadvantage of very rapid evaporation. This makes it insufficient in cases where actual communion is prevented by lack of distillation. And during a very protracted local or genital manipulation this form of substitute must be applied to the vulva, not once, but repeatedly. And this may best, most appropriately and most expeditiously be done without the intermediary offices of the fingers, but through what I prefer to term the *kiss of genital stimulation*, or *genital kiss*, that is, by gentle and soothing caresses with lips and tongue. (Footnote: As all expert readers will easily understand, I have intentionally not employed the more or less technical terms for the attainment of orgasm through buccolingual contact . . . for this reason: I refuse to use these expressions which almost always refer to pathological practices, when I treat of manifestations which are, in their present context, *absolutely unobjectionable and legitimate*, ethically, aesthetically and hygienically.) (Italics ours.)

In similar vein, Dr. Emily Hartshorne, director of the Marriage Council of Philadelphia, reports on a couple who were counseled by the Clinic for a sexual problem, involving the wife's difficulties in achieving orgasm in vaginal coitus. The published case report states that the husband had consciously wanted mouth-genital contact with his wife, but that she had refused. Finally he told the counsellor of a dream in which he was able to satisfy his wife in this way, and she him.

At this point, we read,

> Counsellor explained that oral play was sometimes a part of pre-coital play if both partners desire it. Mr. C. was surprised, having thought it to be a form of perversion.

And in her interpretation of the case, Dr. Hartshorne says,

It is apparent that by divesting the sexual behavior of this couple of right and wrong connotations, the counsellor helped both partners to a healthier attitude.

We fully agree with Dr. Hartshorne's summary of the case that this couple was helped immensely by rectifying their attitudes of *guilt* and *shame* about mouth-genital stimulation. The case is therefore a good example of how wrong one would be in assuming that the mere fact of individuals engaging is various forms of unorthodox sex behavior is any sort of indication that they emotionally accept their own conduct and are free of ethical conflict.

In the case cited above, the wife might, for instance, have been quite willing to engage in the mouth-genital contacts which her husband was demanding, had she not sensed the husband's own negative attitudes about it. One might even speculate whether the husband would not have secretly criticized her, had she submitted earlier to his requests. That this might have been at least partially her motivation for refusing him becomes all the more likely since, as soon as the counseling made mouth-genital play morally and psychologically "safe" for her, she willingly went along with it.

In the marriage counseling case, mouth-genital contacts had apparently been discussed in the context of foreplay. Frequently, that is all that is at stake. In other cases, the woman (or the man, or both partners) desire mouth-genital stimulation to be carried through *to orgasm.*

But mouth-genital contact, even when used only as a foreplay variation, may be of crucial importance in the sex response of some women. They may neither want nor require to be brought to orgasm entirely in this way. Yet they sometimes do need oral stimulation for a sufficient build-up of sexual tension well into the later excitement and plateau phases, but still prefer to be finally brought to orgasm by vaginal intercourse.

One of our informants told us, for instance, that her husband had for years accused her of being frigid and finally of being a Lesbian, because she could not reach orgasm during vaginal intercourse. Her desperation became so great that she even tried to have a Lesbian relationship, to see if this was perhaps the answer to her problems. It was not. However, when her husband went away on a business trip, she took the opportunity to have an affair with another man, and she did achieve orgasm. This other man was the first sex partner who had performed cunnilingus on her during foreplay.

She said:

> I was furious at my husband when I realized that all these years he knew about this technique, but had never told me about it or tried it on me, to see if it would help. All he could do was to fling accusations at me which only made me feel more inferior and insecure.

The case demonstrates again the great significance of oral stimulation for some women; it also points out anew the many emotional obstacles and prejudices which still militate against cunnilingus and fellatio as fully acceptable sex techniques in our society. Yet one cannot escape the fact that for numbers of women, cunnilingus is the most enjoyable form of sexual contact and the one that is most likely to bring them to orgasm.

THE MARRIED LESBIAN

Our Married Lesbian was one of these cases in point. She had never experienced orgasm in any other way. She considered direct genital coitus as nothing but "real road work," which she did not even expect to lead to orgasm. Talking about one of her former lovers with whom she had had her most satisfactory heterosexual experiences, she said:

> He was a very loving man. Almost immediately I was (sexually) happy with him. We always did the same thing, and it

was always successful. We would do 69, I would have orgasm, but he would hold back. Then he would have sexual intercourse with me and he would have orgasm, and I guess he thought I had it again. The justifiable lie. I always emotionally enjoyed sexual intercourse with the people I really loved—particularly with him. Besides, I was gratified, so he could do anything he wanted.

Comparing her sexual relationship with this lover to that with her husband, she ruefully added:

My husband and I never fitted in that respect. We never could do 69, because his torso is too long. We could never get comfortable, whereas this other lover and I just fitted very nicely.

However, our Married Lesbian and her husband had evolved a sex technique which was equally suited to their mutual preferences: they simply perform cunnilingus and fellatio on each other alternately. Only occasionally, "for a change," did they engage in vaginal coitus.

When we inquired of our Married Lesbian about her initial experience in performing fellatio on a man, her first reply was:

I can't remember the first time. I imagine it must have been at somebody's request. . . . Why else should I do it? . . . I've never found male genitalia a thing of beauty or even of much interest to me. . . . But I do remember when it became a steady routine with my first lover . . . the one I really loved.

Later in the interview when talking about something else, she told how on another occasion a man very crudely obliged her to perform fellatio on him.

After this true lover of mine there were a long succession of inappropriate and inadequate substitutes. . . . I remember conducting three love affairs at one time. One of them invited me to dinner one night . . . and sort of pushed me down on my knees and made me do him. Completely unromantic: like an appliance sale.

Apparently this unpleasant experience was not able to prejudice her against the practice of fellatio. In another part of our interview with her she even expressed attitudes of tenderness toward the man's penis and a strange kind of reverse "feeding" symbolism in performing fellatio by which she (and presumably some of her girl friends) had likened the penis to a baby and the woman who was performing fellatio as feeding it.

THE SEXUAL SOPHISTICATE

We would now like to compare what our Sexual Sophisticate had to say about her first experience with performing fellatio and her general feelings about it:

> I still recall the first time I performed fellatio. Up to then I had no knowledge of the existence of this technique. There was no discussion between the two of us, and my lover did not verbally request me to do it. He only gently led me, and I did it almost instinctively.
>
> It amuses me to recall that a previous boy friend had said to me at one time, "Oh, I know of another way to make love," but never told me or showed me what he had in mind. After this first experience with fellatio, I realized that this was what he must have been referring to and which he claimed he had learned from a French prostitute.
>
> The idea of fellatio does not excite me to the extent that I have heard homosexual men rave about it, but I *find it enjoyable, if the man desires it.* To me the most pleasurable part about fellatio is the running of the tongue over the penis. The smooth texture of the glans against the tongue is a sensuous feeling which I enjoy. In addition, the signs of the man's excitement are more stimulating to me than my own part in the act itself.

It is obvious from these statements and those of the other women we quoted, as well as from our other interview data, that many women do find the performance of fellatio pleasant, but not as sexually exciting as seems to be the case with that group of men who really like to perform cunnilingus. This is where Kinsey's findings and our own observations on this matter meet.

It also appears from that section of our interviews which dealt with Anglo-American women that even those who do like to perform fellatio are troubled by problems involving the male ejaculate, although this was less true of European women. In addition, the matter is further complicated by the fact that some men equate the woman's hesitancy or refusal to go "all the way" in this technique with a personal rejection which can result in unnecessary tensions and misunderstandings.

THE DOCTOR'S WIFE

Some of the couples we had interviewed had found mouth-genital techniques less suitable to them because they interfered with factors which were essential to their personal enjoyment in sexual relations. As one example among many, we shall quote what the Doctor's Wife had to say about this matter:

> We have tried the 69 position several times, but there is something about the *lack of contact* in that position which bothers us. We are *so used to asking one another to do this, or to do that during intercourse,* and that's just impossible doing 69.

What the Doctor's Wife is trying to say in the above quoted statement is that she and her husband were relying heavily on the stimulation supplied by mutual sex talk and that this was made nearly impossible in mouth-genital techniques.

However, in our experience and observations, cunnilingus is the sex technique which is more likely than any other to bring many women to orgasm who fail to respond sufficiently to other stimulation techniques. This also seems to be implied in some of Kinsey's statements about the relative merits of various sex techniques.

Finally, we wanted to understand better what a woman's subjective experience of cunnilingus might be like, what her physical sensations during cunnilingus are, and how they compare with those experienced under other types of sexual stimulation.

This sort of testimony was extremely difficult to obtain. Of the hundreds of women whom we interviewed only *one* was able to make meaningful statements about her feelings during oral stimulation of her genitals: the Sexual Sophisticate.

THE SEXUAL SOPHISTICATE

She alone was able to describe adequately the sensations that she had experienced during cunnilingus and to point out its relative advantages and disadvantages from her point of view as a woman:

The body sensations during cunnilingus are different from those I have in intercourse. *Sometimes it is easier for me to come to orgasm this way*, as I can concentrate more on my bodily sensations. During intercourse, I sometimes start worrying about my partner, wondering whether he is enjoying it, whether he is about to come to orgasm, what he wants me to do, and so on. In cunnilingus, I forget all this and just let the other person do to me what he wants. This gives me a thrill of suspense as I'm not quite sure how and where he will start and what he will do. Sometimes I get a little annoyed, if he doesn't hit the spot which is the most sensitive, or if he doesn't apply enough pressure long enough in the right place.

I think a man has to be sure of himself to perform cunnilingus well, probably even more so than in intercourse, because *any hesitation really kills it*. It helps, when the man presses with one hand on the pubis which puts more pressure on the genitals and pushes the clitoris down closer to the opening of the vagina. The running of the tongue gently around and over the clitoris is a teasing sort of titillation which is fine to begin with, but the more excited one becomes and the closer to orgasm one gets, the more force one needs. At that point, I feel like pushing my partner's head down harder or lifting my hips up higher to make the pressure greater.

When the man takes the clitoris between his lips and sucks on it, it feels as if something was rhythmically pulling it. I've never had orgasm right at that moment, though this sucking technique definitely helps to get one ready for it. One can also get a tremendous feeling when the man moves his head rapidly back and forth or sideways, always keeping his mouth on the clitoris.

I think each time I experience cunnilingus, I desire it a little differently. Sometimes I want the man to run his tongue along the labia and put it in the vagina, while at other times I want him just to stay on the clitoris.

The changes in rhythm are important too. Sometimes I want to scream "faster, faster!" while on other occasions I like the lazy slow motion, the gentle feeling of the tongue barely touching the clitoris. Other times, I want my partner to put a finger in the vagina, press the upper part and hold it there while he is performing cunnilingus. The constant pressure, I think, is better than moving the finger in and out. But in certain positions one gets the pressure of the chin against the outside of the vagina and the labia and that adds to the pleasure. At still other times, I like to have the man hold my buttocks while performing cunnilingus which gives one the benefit of having another area stimulated simultaneously.

I think it is too bad that nature has made it impossible for the man to perform cunnilingus at the same time that he has the penis in the vagina. I am sure the sensation would be out of this world. I usually want the man to put his penis in as soon as I've had orgasm and then continue to have intercourse, culminating in another orgasm.

I notice that if I squat over the man's head, I can make more pelvic movements and have better control over the pressure. But I find I don't always relax as much that way as when I'm lying down. Besides, I find the position can become tiring if it goes on for a long time, though it is obviously much more comfortable for the man.

Looking back over our Sexual Sophisticate's statements about cunnilingus and fellatio, we find that she is enthusiastically in support of cunnilingus as one of her favorite sources of stimulation. She is reserved, yet positive in her estimate of fellatio as one of those things which a woman might—to a point—enjoy doing, but which she does mainly for the benefit of the man. In contrast to all this, she did not have much good to say about the combination of the two techniques, known as the 69 position:

> The 69 position is in my book another of those that is for the young and athletic. To have cunnilingus and fellatio separately is always a pleasure, but when one attempts to do them simultaneously, it can become just plain hard work. If the woman is on top, she has to balance herself on her knees and one hand while holding the penis with the other. This makes vigorous movements difficult and tiring. I have found myself unable to enjoy what is happening to my body, as I am fully occupied performing fellatio and giving my partner pleasure.
>
> When the man is on top, I am able to lie back and relax, but I'm frustrated by not being able to freely move my head which is necessary if one wants to do fellatio well. More threatening, of course, is that one loses control over how deep to let the penis penetrate into the mouth since one cannot move one's head back freely as is possible when one is on top. The main problem remains the same, whether I am on top or underneath in the 69 position: I simply cannot enjoy the man performing cunnilingus on me and at the same time get ready for orgasm, if I have to simultaneously perform fellatio on him.

These feelings of the Sexual Sophisticate about the 69 position are, as one will remember, quite the opposite to those of the Married Lesbian. That informant had said that she had enjoyed this technique very much and had found it extremely successful with a former lover of hers, while she had not found it practical with her husband for anatomical reasons.

In general terms, considering the objections to mouth-genital contacts from a psychological point of view, one can distinguish basically two main complexes at the root of most of them: 1) the genitals and their secretions are associated with the organs and products of excretion; mouth-genital practices are therefore often considered "dirty" and "animalistic"; 2) mouth-genital contacts are unconsciously (and sometimes consciously) condemned as ends in themselves because they do not lead to procreation; this type of criticism is implied in the notion that mouth-genital contacts are "unnatural."

We have already discussed the first mentioned source of prejudice earlier in this section. As to the second contention that mouth-genital contacts are "unnatural" one can only gain one's point by losing it: if one states the fact that mouth-genital behavior is very common in all mammalian species and can therefore hardly be considered "unnatural," one is told that this just proves it to be "animalistic."

But regardless of whether some people consider mouth-genital contacts "animalistic," "unnatural," or worse, the experts today agree that these techniques are not only harmless, but highly recommendable as a major source of sexual stimulation. It is therefore predictable that oral stimulation techniques will eventually outlive the antiquated repressive laws and the already waning social prejudice against them.

XII

Mental Aphrodisiacs

I<small>T</small> is certain that erotic stimulation for women starts before the act itself, but the taboos against feminine sexual enjoyment are such that most women do not like to admit that they are responsive to music, novels, movies, nudity, home-made erotica, clothes, boudoir atmosphere, pornographic films, theater, burlesque or the many other stimulants, deliberately erotic or not, which constitute visual or mental aids to sex. But the fact is that the question is not even *whether* women are susceptible to such psychological sex stimuli as sexy books and "naughty" pictures, but how much more or less susceptible they are than men.

Kinsey himself did not seem to think that the majority of women were able to respond as strongly to sexual intangibles as men, though his own statistics should have shown him that he was underrating female capacity in this respect. His figures showed that fully *one third* of the women in his sample responded similarly to men with regard to a variety of erotica, including the watching of such supposedly all-male entertainment as burlesque and stag movies. And between *two* and *three* per cent of the women responded, to everybody's surprise, even more positively to a large number of assorted erotica than *any* of the men in his sample!

Proof that the "lust of the eye" is not exclusive to the male has also come from other, and sometimes the least suspected quarters.

A bizarre instance of this kind occurred in 1949 in connection with the arrest of a dancer. In this case, one of the two vice squad ladies making the arrest (interestingly and significantly the married one) admitted that watching another woman do an erotic dance got her sexually excited, while the other woman implied that she too might have been affected had it not been for her advanced age of forty-five! (The Justice of the Peace, however, correctly pointed out that the persons making the complaint had different standards from those attending night clubs regularly, that no one was forced to attend against his will, and therefore released the dancer.)

Turning to more serious evidence of women's voyeuristic potential, female anthropologist Hortense Powdermaker tells us that Lesu women may actually become sufficiently aroused by psychological stimuli to need some kind of erotic outlet, if no male partner happens to be present.

> A woman will masturbate if she is sexually excited and there is no man to satisfy her. *A couple may be having intercourse in the same house, or near enough for her to see them*, and she may thus become aroused.

Dr. Powdermaker was not surprised by this finding, as her matter-of-fact statement would seem to indicate: still to us it appears rather significant, because it is generally denied that women can be aroused by such sights and to this extent.

There exist, however, a number of older European as well as Chinese and Japanese pictures, showing women in the act of masturbating while watching the erotic activities of others. Granted these stories and illustrations are for the most part the products of male artists and writers, it is still difficult to believe that they represent just so many projections of men's own fantasies without any basis in fact whatsoever. Instead, one is forced to assume that these examples reflect a shift in sexual customs and that under different social conditions, female voyeurism was more evident at one time in Europe and Japan than it is today.

But the apparent reaction of the majority of modern women in our society to the idea of psychological sex stimuli is perhaps best reflected by a statement of Maxine Davis, who says:

> Erotic art and literature, whatever their quality, may give her (modern woman) a fillip to which *she responds with sexual sensations in her female organs.* They may stimulate her imagination to a certain extent *especially while she is still young,* but later they either interest her, leave her indifferent or actually repelled, depending on her standards . . . A few things she sees or hears or thinks may cause an erotic response, but not many. The average woman evokes these psychic stimuli as a rule only when she resorts to a sexual outlet other than in intercourse. (Italics ours.)

We cannot agree more with Maxine Davis in her statement that all kinds of erotica may give "many women a fillip." It could also be true that in our society younger girls (and, we may add, younger boys as well) may be more interested in erotica than older people but only, we believe, if one is think-ing of what we call "hard-core" pornography. But what does this mean?

It appears that younger people in our society are interested in pornography for basically two reasons: 1) to satisfy their *curiosity* about those aspects of sexuality on which even the most progressive parental or public sex education still with-holds information (especially about actual techniques of love-making or what the psychiatrist Harry Stack Sullivan called the "lust mechanism" in sex), and 2) as *substitutes* for more direct sex outlets.

This seems to be what the female psychoanalyst whom we consulted referred to:

> I haven't seen much pornography . . . Only once or twice. *When I was young,* maybe in the late teens or early twenties, I was very much excited by these things, *especially since I didn't have any direct sexual experience.* I must say that now in my later years, these things don't mean much to me, really.

One must balance this type of statement with that of other women who have had their first contact with pornography in their youth, but who retained interest in it throughout their adult lives. Among the hundreds of women whom we interviewed, the female psychoanalyst was actually the *only* one who spoke of a decreasing interest, with age, in erotica (and this probably because she was, as she said, largely unacquainted with them).

Of the four women whose sex histories we are using as the basis of our study, the Sexual Sophisticate—in contrast to the Female Psychoanalyst—had had *no* contact with pornography in her youth, but developed an abiding interest in it in her late twenties, which was superseded in her case only by a stronger interest in erotica of greater artistic merit.

The More-Than-Average Housewife who did have only one isolated contact with pornography in her mid-teens, kept a lively interest in it over the years:

> When I was fifteen I was sitting with some of the boys in their car during lunch hour at school. They had a film of intercourse in all different positions, homosexuality, fellatio, three or four men and women doing it together, and one with a donkey. We held it up to the light, wishing that we had a projector. *This helped me* and, of course, *excited* me. Later a fellow told me about shows with animals. . . .

What she means is that seeing some of the pictures in the pornographic movie helped her in making the mechanics of sexual intercourse clearer to her, while at the same time exciting her sexually. There is no indication in her statement, nor in the sex histories of the majority of the other women we interviewed, that seeing such pictures had been a great shock and upsetting to them. They either liked them or didn't like them, and in neither case did the one seem worse off for it than the other.

It is undoubtedly true, as Maxine Davis suggests, that women resort more often to erotica (in the widest sense) as take-offs for auto-erotic fantasies than as preparation for sexual intercourse. This is also true for men. But in cultures other than our own, for instance in classical China and Japan, and to a lesser extent in India and the Near East, it has traditionally been the custom for couples to use erotic pictures and books as a prelude to or even during sexual relations. We know this to be the case not only from Oriental sex manuals which highly recommend this practice, but also from some of the erotic Chinese and Japanese pictures themselves. Frequently, they show couples reading erotic stories together or viewing erotic illustrations during sexual foreplay and intercourse. It is clear from these illustrations that the couples are not merely learning or satisfying curiosity.

The joint use of erotica by husband and wife is magnificently and humorously decribed in an ancient Chinese novel, dealing with the life of a talented young scholar and his wife Jade Perfume. The story describes the husband as having, besides his thirst for knowledge, an equally insatiable desire for sensual pleasure, and how he manages to "corrupt" his originally chaste and virtuous wife with the aid of a series of such erotic paintings. When the wife at first objects to the pictures saying, "What is the use of looking at such an unorthodox thing?" the husband corrects her with the following severe lecture:

> If this really were an unorthodox thing, why then should the artist have painted it? On the contrary, this album represents the most orthodox thing which has existed since the creation of the universe. That is why great artists have depicted it in full colors and mounted these pictures with fine silk. Such albums are sold in antique shops and great scholars keep them upon their shelves, so that the people of later ages may know the right way of doing this. But for such albums, the reason of sexual intercourse would gradually fall into oblivion. Husbands would abandon their spouses and wives turn their backs on their men. The line of creation would be broken and mankind would disappear . . . Learning how to conceive and become

pregnant and give birth to sons and daughters, this certainly belongs to the study of the Right Way!

Finally, the husband's eloquence convinces Jade Perfume that she should consent to look at the album, and her husband lets her sit on his knees, so they can inspect the pictures together. He also volunteers to read out loud the difficult accompanying text to her in order to teach her the spirit of the pictures and so that they would later be able to put these examples to practice. Jade Perfume's passion becomes aroused by the pictures and stories and she winds up as much given to erotic pleasures as the husband who had seduced her.

We could cite many examples from our own culture to show that a considerable proportion of Western couples use various psychological aphrodisiacs in much the same way as was once the common practice in the Orient. Moreover, the statements of many of the women whom we interviewed leave no doubt that in these cases the erotica used had a similarly stimulating effect on them as they had on their husbands. Three of the four main subjects in this study have expressed themselves most unmistakably on this point.

THE DOCTOR'S WIFE

Talking about the use of erotica in the general context of foreplay to intercourse, the Doctor's Wife said:

> Most of the time we play around with each other for some time before actually starting intercourse. I don't think there is anything worse than to be flopped on the back by a guy and jumped on when you're still half cold. We like to take our time, trying various maneuvers. Sometimes, though, if we've been *reading* something exciting together, or been *talking* ourselves into the mood, and we're all ready to go, we just go ahead, because *I think the (mental) stimulation is just as good as the foreplay*.

The Doctor's Wife was one of the women in our sample who respond very strongly to words, as, for instance, her reference to "talking ourselves into the mood" indicates. In another part of our interview with her, this not uncommon response among women is expressed even more clearly:

> . . . My husband is very clever in getting me into the mood. He was the first man I knew who was smart enough to use words to get me excited. He might just stand a distance away from me and say, How would you like to do this thing or the other . . .? That always gets me excited.

Once again we must refer to the sexual wisdom of the Orient where the use of *erotic conversation* was deliberately and widely used before and during intercourse. Even as late as 1951 it is recommended in Abul Hasnat's sex manual, *Sex Love and Happy Marriage*:

> If sexually exciting conversation is carried on before and spicy stories are told during sexual union, production of orgasm in the wife will be easy.

The Doctor's Wife and her husband used a variety of other mental aphrodisiacs during sexual intercourse which were obviously enjoyed by both of them and which she described as follows:

> We've tried different things too, with *mirrors*, different *lights*, and so on. Sometimes I like to *dress up* in black theater stockings or special lingerie . . . or I put on real tight *leotards* without a top, and high heels . . . I like to do this especially when my husband doesn't expect it, and just come into the living room at night or into the den when he's reading or working. That sort of thing sends him so that he can hardly make it into the bedroom. Frankly, the dressing up and seeing him get so excited, gets me all worked up too. . . .

Asked what kind of readings she preferred for erotic stimulation, the Doctor's Wife answered:

> Oh, not the usual soap opera type of love story I used to enjoy as a kid. We have some pornography, but I don't like some of that either. So I just read the parts I like and skip over

the other stuff. I get nauseated when they start dragging in kids, and some of the other things. . . .

We have often found it to be true that many women react in much the same negative manner as the Doctor's Wife to pornographic stories or pictures involving unsavory sexual situations, and especially those which include the participation of children. This reaction on the part of an undoubtedly larger proportion of women than men is, however, quite understandable and need not be taken as a sign of their lesser interest in erotica per se. To the contrary, it is all the more remarkable that many women, like our informant, can critically assess these serious ethical, psychological, and aesthetic defects of the common run of pornographic representations and stories, without failing to respond or of rejecting them altogether.

The More-Than-Average Housewife

Quite a different slant is given to the reading of erotic stories (not necessarily pornography) by the More-Than-Average Housewife:

> My husband thinks everything's great when you are well fed, well frocked and well loved, and he's got a point. But I do get sick of making clothes over and cutting boys' hair, economizing on everything. Maybe that's partly why I enjoy sexy books—it at least gets my mind off problems, and on something I like.

It appears from this humorous confession that our informant uses sex and sexual stimuli almost as a sort of opium with which to escape from unpleasant reality. And why not? There is little enough joy in life, and if erotic pleasure in reading can, at least for a moment, lift a person out of depressing everyday routine, so much the better. Perhaps it is just this particular function of eroticism which is one of the greatest and least recognized of its blessings.

In sex it is only a small step from the sublime to the ridiculous, and vice versa, as every experienced person knows. And this is equally, and for similar reasons, true in the contemplation of nature, art, and music. The transcendental and the human, and often the all-too-human, come to border on one another, and the end effect depends on which elements will gain the upper hand.

In the case of our More-Than-Average Housewife, this relationship between the all-too-human and the sublime is evident in her remarks about the erotic effect of music on her:

> I can feel excited by a song I like, for instance, on the car radio. And even though one feels spiritually elevated by music, essentially it's a *sensual* feeling. I know that somehow a man will take care of that feeling at some future date.

Likewise, the manner in which she speaks of her erotic feelings when in contact with nature does not lack in equally serious as well as humorous overtones:

> . . . Have you ever run nude in the woods, or ran nude through the rain? This to me is an exhilarating, passionately exalting feeling and even more so if you know that not far behind is a man, bent on the chase, and he'll catch you and probably throw you.
>
> Or when I swim nude—this is to me a feeling beyond description. I feel a freedom unhampered by anything. It makes me ready. It is probably the daring freedom of it. If it's a party of say ten or twenty nude men and women and one man is particularly attentive and touching me, this for sure sets me up. Or lying on the beach, clothed, but preferably not, looking up at the stars and the moon, I feel so small but also so vigorous, so healthy, and if there happens to be an honest-to-god man beside me, I feel it twice as fiercely, because it excites me to see any virile, masculine man in the nude.

This description of running out into the rain naked, with a man in pursuit, certainly is reminiscent of the famous rain

scene in *Lady Chatterley's Lover*. Whether influenced by
reading D. H. Lawrence's novel or not, our More-Than-
Average Housewife seems to be particularly responsive to the
sexual stimulation of nature, but unfortunately, her husband
did not share her enthusiasm for outdoor erotica. As she
sadly remarked:

> I've been trying for months to have my husband put a mat-
> tress out in the backyard, as the sky and woods always have
> thrilled me, but it doesn't excite him.

We have interviewed quite a few women who spoke of
similar wishes and experiences. They freely admitted that the
intimate contact and feeling of oneness with nature could
have an immensely stimulating effect on them. This is perhaps one of the reasons why in antiquity, the bacchanalia
generally took place in the open, perhaps in a meadow, on a
hill, or in a clearing in the woods.

Our More-Than-Average Housewife was, however, not all
nature girl. She and her husband were weaving certain erotic
fantasies which they hoped to put into practice some time in
the future and which might sound rather "debauched" to
many ears. These plans and fantasies included a variety of
unorthodox activities, to which we have already alluded
earlier and about which our informant spoke as follows:

> We've talked about how we'd like to see some exhibitions
> and a few pornographic movies, and get into a group of con-
> genial couples and swap mates for an evening. Oh, yes, we
> were going to join a nudist colony, but as yet haven't done any
> of it. Well, when the kids leave home, we'll try some of those.
> So you see, *due to economics and our kids we are kept pretty
> well on the straight and narrow*, and not due to laws, or in-
> hibitions or our upbringing. Honest to gosh, with P.T.A.,
> scouts, work, chauffeuring kids, sports, I forgot church, and
> all the other duties one goes through to do what I suppose
> is right for community, country, God and our children it's
> a damn wonder there's any time left for wooing and making
> love.

Most unconventionally, our informant speaks in the same breath about some of the socially most unacceptable sex behavior and her work with parent-teacher associations, civic groups, and church.

What does this sort of thing show? We think it demonstrates that very ordinary people who are engaged in very ordinary occupations and who otherwise blend well into the rest of the community may have very extraordinary sex fantasies and are liable to engage in very unorthodox sex practices. Members of the more conservative classes frequently do not realize that substantial minorities in the community, including people with whom they live and work, hold considerably different sex standards than they do. (This unawareness of differing moral standards among people who normally operate in separate sub-groups within the larger culture may then lead to truly embarrassing moments and sometimes to serious interpersonal friction when they are suddenly thrown together and asked to interact and communicate on matters involving ethical judgments.)

In another instance, the same woman tells in some comical detail and disarming honesty how she and her husband had produced their own pornography with the aid of a Polaroid camera.

I forgot the year of the Polaroid camera. My husband got me one for my birthday about five years ago. We took pictures of each other in all ways of undress and partial dress, the way he likes it. I took some pictures of him when he was erect, sitting, standing, and so forth. Then we set it on time-exposure and took pictures in various stages of intercourse. These pictures, I tell you, are hard to shoot. It takes an hour to get the camera where you want it and you have to get on and off to check the range—by then you've got to have an orgasm. Finally, we thought of setting up the camera long before and I'd get him to lie down to check the range.

He kept my pictures in his wallet, including a few of intercourse. He said the pictures did him a lot of good when he was on trips. I felt they were holding down his roving nature.

I kept his pictures and a few of intercourse for myself when he was away. However, since we have moved around so much, he was afraid they'd get lost. Also, the kids might find them, and if we both had an accident, they would be found by some-one else. So we burned all but about eight nudes of me and one showing him with an erection. But to hell with dying, I think we shall take some more photos next summer.

Lest it be thought that home-made pornography is some-thing very unusual, we hasten to add that we have spoken to several other American and European couples and individuals who had taken similar pictures, and some who had even made amateur pornographic movies of themselves. This should per-haps be less surprising than it is to many people, if one re-members that as children many of us have produced our own crude erotica in obscene wall scribblings and drawings. After all, does not every imaginative couple use themselves as mental aphrodisiacs at some time or other, even if no cameras are involved?

THE MARRIED LESBIAN

We see this, for instance, more poetically expressed in an unpublished autobiographical story by our Married Lesbian:

Later, we made love in an extraordinary fashion for a mar-ried couple. If my husband did not carry me, because, out of habit I anticipated his gestures, he guided me with a lover's gentleness into my dressing room where the vanity, laden with my perfumes, my jewelry, my little intimate belongings, was completely surrounded by mirrors from floor to ceiling. That triple exposure was made possible by closet doors that could be adjusted like those of a fashionable modiste, so that no part of you escaped notice in the course of your toilet. . . . It was my husband's desire to make love to me there, so that he could dwell on an infinite number of images of the two of us . . . each image slightly different, because of the angle of reflec-tion . . . in the most intimate and passionate of embraces. I realized that he was beginning to share with me the inordinate pleasures he had cultivated with Yvonne, that he now wanted to train me to that visual appreciation of the act of love to which both of them had become so addicted. . . .

If the visual stimuli were more for the benefit of the husband than for herself, she did find certain writings (*not* pornography) sexually exciting.

> I think I get more excited through reading, if anything. The love scenes in Proust always stimulated me very much. *Lolita* did to a certain extent—the initial seduction scene in the hotel. Also something I read in a French book . . . something about a society girl who got hard up for money in the south of France. Being desperately in need of money, she performs in a sort of peep show with another woman. . . .

As a result of these readings, she said, she had at times satisfied herself auto-erotically.

The Sexual Sophisticate

Most explicit about her reactions to a wide variety of mental aphrodisiacs is the Sexual Sophisticate. This is no accident. We had specifically asked her to be detailed, because we had expected that her professional training and ability for self-observation were likely to throw more light on these obscure aspects of woman's psychological sex response. After arranging her material according to the various topics or categories into which it naturally falls, we present it here just as she expressed herself on these matters:

> Novels, autobiographies, or even some scientific reports, dealing with sex have always been able to arouse me at times sexually. On the other hand, my sexual response to erotic art, such as the temple sculpture of India or the erotic scenes in paintings and drawings by such artists as Courbet, Goya, and Picasso represents a taste which I acquired only over time.
> I find books of Henry Miller, Casanova's Memoirs and many others extremely exciting, though novels are generally less interesting to me than autobiographic writings. I do *not* ap-

preciate the magazine-type love stories, because of their extreme sentimentality and moralism.

I must confess, I can remember times when I have been erotically stimulated by reading certain sections of marriage manuals. There are passages even in the Kinsey studies, aside from the duller statistical parts, which have been erotically stimulating to me.

Unfortunately, I have never acquired a connoisseur's taste in poetry. But the love poems of John Donne and Herrick definitely have an erotic effect on me, as they must have had on the women to whom they were originally addressed.

Reading sex jokes (or hearing them told) usually amuses, but doesn't excite me. On the other hand, some sexy, but humorous folk songs and sea chanties I have heard do have a certain erotic appeal to me.

Some plays have an erotic effect on me, for instance, Jean Genet's *The Balcony*, Tennessee Williams' *Cat on a Hot Tin Roof*, and several others. . . .

We had particularly asked how she reacted to the male type of physical culture magazines showing male nudes in various poses:

I think it is unfortunate that these muscle magazines show men who are obviously so much in love with themselves and their bodies that it is impossible for me to imagine a relationship with them. I aesthetically appreciate well built men, and I think pictures of healthy looking specimens of male nudes who are not quite so muscle-bound and in less grotesque and more natural poses would have a greater erotic effect on me than the ones I have seen in these magazines. But after all, I realize that type of magazine is put out for the benefit of men and not for women.

As for nudist magazines, I know that nudists are generally quite conservative sexually, but still when looking at their magazines I do sometimes find myself becoming erotically interested. A nice looking nude body does that to me. Of other magazines (*not* nudist publications) showing nudes, I like those from the Scandinavian countries best. Unlike the British, French, and American pictures, they show the genitals with the pubic hair which, I think, makes the picture more natural and attractive. The pubic hair simply seems to belong to the adult human form, and if it is not there, or if all or part of the genitals themselves are brushed out, one gets the feeling that something is missing; in fact, I'd say, in that case the whole genital region looks deformed. I can only compare those touched-up pictures to the lifeless display mannequins that one sees when a show window is being redecorated; so artificial and unnatural.

Nude photos in which the pubic hair is not shown or where the genital region is blanked out do not only look unnatural, as our informant stated, but they can be positively *upsetting*, both to adults and to children. (This is precisely one of the reasons why, in play therapy with children, clinicians use specially made, uncastrated dolls, including the genitals.)

The same informant told us about her visit to a museum in which, as she said, "all the male statues had plaster fig leaves added":

> Looking at these beautiful Greek and Roman statues which had been mutilated by covering the genitals with fig leaves, I suddenly realized that there are still those who'd prefer that all humans were *neuters*. My reaction to this museum was one of utter revulsion and disgust. For the first time I experienced what obscenity and perversion really meant. These beautiful statues of the human body had become truly obscene to me, because of the superfluous appendages on which one was almost forced to fixate.
>
> On the other hand, on statues where the genitals are freely shown, my eyes have never been fixated on any part of the body. In these cases, I find myself reacting to the genitals as part of the whole human form, like the legs, arms, hands, etc. It was only because somebody before me had decided that this part of the body was obscene that I found myself becoming just as obsessed by it as the censor must have been to have thought of it first.

These remarks touch not only on problems involving aesthetics, but also on questions involving public morality and censorship. Our informant correctly points out that if the purpose of censorship was the preservation of "decency" and avoidance of a morbid interest in sex, the suppression of the pubic hair or the genital region simply tends to produce the opposite effect.

We asked what particular works of sculpture had a special erotic appeal for this informant:

> Michelangelo's "David" is one of the most sexually stimulating sights to me. If I ask myself what is so exciting about this statue, I would say first of all the muscles around the abdomen, the strength in the arms and legs, the tautness of the buttocks, the beauty of the head, and many other details. I would like to add that *for me the inclusion of the penis and the testicles in a work of art are needed* to complete the wholesomeness and handsomeness of the male body.
>
> After Michelangelo's "David" the works of Rodin are erotically the most exciting to me. Even as a young girl, I never failed to respond to the diffuse sensuality in Rodin's statues, as, for example, in "The Kiss" and many others. The human bodies in his works seem to be always in the most erotic positions. Also his technique of leaving many of his statues unfinished in the rough matrix strikes me as highly seductive as I follow in my mind how the texture changes from a very rough surface to skin-like smoothness. Incidentally, I also find Rodin's drawings or sketches of nude models of dancers, often with their legs wide apart and genitals showing, both aesthetically pleasing and erotically stimulating.

We asked whether she found the female body in statues as exciting as the male:

> Comparing my reactions to the male and female body in art, *I find the female body in statues just as erotic as the male body.* As with the male statues, it is the play of the muscles, this time around the breasts and the lower pelvic region.

This reaction seems to indicate a sex difference between the male and female response to the nude form: we have never heard a heterosexual male state that statues of male nudes held about equal stimulation value for him as representations of the female form. The difference is possibly based on the greater ability of women to feel themselves into a male erotic response, as well as experiencing their own. It may also be due to the woman's identification with the female form (in the artistic representation or in nature) and imagining herself in this way being erotically perceived by the male: but these are only two of the many hypotheses concerning the psychology of woman's sex response which should be confirmed or disproved by controlled experiments.

Furthermore, our Sexual Sophisticate preferred to add stimulation through the sense of *touch* which heightened the total erotic effect for her.

> If I am allowed to *feel* the sculpture, in addition to *seeing it*, I find myself responding even more.

We now asked about her reactions to films, both documentary and general:

> In contrast to the general run of feature films, I have found quite a few documentary and art films erotically quite exciting. I remember, for instance, a highly artistic documentary film, *The Geography of the Human Body*, which by the clever and imaginative use of special photographic techniques had almost the same erotic stimulation value to me as any outright pornographic film that I have ever seen.
>
> Even after an interval of two or three years, several scenes from that film stand out clearly in my mind: A close-up of the wetting of the lips by the tip of the tongue in which the tongue really caresses the lips like a lover, with pearls of saliva added to make it even more sensuous; a shot of the armpit with the axillary hair, strongly suggestive of the genital region with the pubic hair; and especially a full-screen view of the navel which, through the trick of photographic enlargement, gives the perfect illusion of the exterior female sex organs, seen at very close range.
>
> Other documentary films that have had an erotic effect on me include a film showing animals, such as minks, cats, porcupines, horses, etc. in the act of copulation. In that film, I found the quick, vigorous, thrusting movements of the copulating

animals extremely exciting, as well as their pre-coital and post-coital behavior, especially the licking of their own or their mate's genitals.

If I were to say which animals in that film were the most exciting to me as they were shown mating, I would unhesitatingly name the stallion and his mare. Next to the mating of horses, I would say that the humorous grace and delicacy of the male porcupine as he approaches the female for copulation and her receptive lifting of the quilled tail were among the most fascinating scenes in the film. The slow, almost deliberate copulatory movements of the male porcupine, as he stands almost totally erect behind the female, make their whole mating process a kind of slow-motion ballet of great charm.

In fact, I would say that *I much prefer a good documentary* on animal mating to most pornographic films.

We have come to the conclusion that the sight of animal mating seems to have at least as much erotic appeal to women as it has to men. In the erotic art of Europe, especially that of the seventeenth and eighteenth centuries, and also in Chinese and Japanese pictures, one often sees women secretly watching the mating of doves, dogs, or cattle. Erotic literature also abounds in descriptions of mating animals, particularly of horses (for instance, detailed description of the mating of horses fills several pages in the famous *Memoirs of a Singer* whose author was in all likelihood a woman, the pre-World War I Austrian singing star Wilhelmine Schroeder-Devrient).

Even some of the most aristocratic ladies in old England seem to have been highly susceptible to the exciting spectacle which the breeding of horses may provide, as historical sources would indicate. Quoting from Bruno Partridge's *A History of Orgies* we read:

> She was a beautiful ladie and . . . very salacious, and she had a contrivance that in the spring of the yeare, when the stallions were to leap the mares, they were to be brought before such a part of the house where she had a *vidette* to look on them and please herself with this sport: and then she would act the like sport herself with *her* stallions. One of her great gallants was crooke-back't Cecill earl of Salisbury.

Our Sexual Sophisticate's account further refers to her reactions to pornographic films and still photos, and finally to burlesque and other erotic dances. Starting with her impressions of pornographic films, she says:

> I happen to have seen a good number of pornographic films, and most of them left technically and aesthetically much to be desired. Yet, I must confess that I generally find the direct intercourse scenes in pornographic films, and the sexual group activities which are often part of the plot, erotically exciting. But one sequence of a pornographic film which I saw some time ago still remains quite vividly in my mind: it concerned a girl skilfully performing fellatio on her partner. When the situation was changed, and the man was performing cunnilingus on the girl, it did not have nearly the same degree of erotic excitement for me. I find myself reacting postively to the semen and lubrication which is often shown on the genitals of the people during intercourse. I have noticed the same reaction on my part while reading about the sexual discharges in pornographic stories. On the other hand, close-ups of the man's ejaculation outside the vagina that I have seen in pornographic films and photos have left me cold.
>
> A disturbing element in pornographic films which can ruin much of the effect for me is the fact that frequently one or the other of the male "actors" seems to be having difficulty in achieving an erection, or sustaining it through parts of the film. Equally distracting to me can be the fact that some of the models in these pictures look so downright unhappy and miserable. Nevertheless, to be perfectly honest, *I have never yet sat through a pornographic film which was not at least to some degree erotically stimulating to me,* regardless of how poor its quality might have been. However, I have usually noticed that just a *few minutes of a pornographic film are sufficient for maximum erotic benefit.*

If the Sexual Sophisticate remarked that pornographic films can become somewhat boring after a while, some men have expressed similar reactions. Her criticism represents therefore probably a reaction to the generally poor quality of pornographic films rather than a genuine sex difference.

We note that the Sexual Sophisticate found the film sequence of a girl performing fellatio on a man more exciting than a sequence showing cunnilingus. This is the reverse of the reaction of most men who seem to prefer scenes of cunnilingus. The psychological sex difference lies probably in the woman's reaction to the sight of the erect penis. As our informant said, when asked directly about this, *"Why, sure—in cunnilingus there is nothing to see!"*

On the other hand, she could not appreciate film sequences of pictures showing the male ejaculation outside the vagina. This could be due to the fact that only a man could have a *visceral* reaction to such pictures, while a woman would have no physiological experience with which to connect it.

Continuing with her reactions to various visual sex stimuli, our informant compared pornographic still photos with pornographic films:

> Anything without movement does not stir me nearly as much as that which includes movement, such as films or dancing. This makes for one strike against pornographic still photos right from the beginning. The only pornographic photos which I did find more pleasant—though still not as exciting as films—were some of the older ones, taken in the early 1900's. In these photos, the men and women were obviously enjoying themselves and not just enduring the process as in the majority of modern pornographic photos that I have seen. Actually, in the older photos, the smiles of the women and some of the poses give these pictures a dreamlike, surrealistic quality, which adds greatly to their peculiar charm for me.

No less provocative than our informant's statements about pornographic films and pictures were her comments on *burlesque* and other erotic forms of dance. Bluntly and factually she stated:

> I think I enjoy good burlesque almost as much as any man. What is erotically most exciting to me in burlesque is my

identification with the dancer. First of all I find watching the very movements of the dance stimulating, almost to the same degree as when I am dancing with a partner who is a good dancer.

Secondly, I find the mounting tension and excitement of the audience a stimulant to my own sexual arousal. If I were not such a shy person, I think the occupation of a top burlesque dancer (such as Lily St. Cyr or Gypsy Rose Lee) could be an enjoyable one. Of course, the smoky, depressing places in which burlesque is often held and much of the other unpleasantness associated with the entertainment field would spoil much of the pleasure for me. But in spite of all this, I almost invariably feel some degree of sexual excitement while watching a burlesque or a good sexy floor show.

When I visited Egypt, one of the things I was anxious to see was genuine Egyptian belly dancing. When I mentioned this desire to one of my Egyptian friends, he took me to one of the lower-class open air restaurants in Cairo where many of the farmers from the surrounding countryside congregate at night for some gay entertainment. In these places, I was told, the belly dancing was much more authentic than in the plush Western-style night clubs of the city.

I was not disappointed, for in spite of the primitive surroundings the dancing was excellent. I was absolutely fascinated and envied the dancers' control over their bodies and the pleasure they must be deriving from it. In addition, I would find it very stimulating to be able to arouse the male audience in this fashion.

I have even found the transvestite type of floor shows, such as Finocchio's in San Francisco or the Carousel in Paris exciting. On the other hand, I don't believe I am reacting to the same things in these shows that a transvestite or homosexual might find stimulating. The idea of a man dressing up in women's clothes holds absolutely no fascination for me. If anything, the opposite would be the case.

I am identifying as a woman with the "women" performers on the stage, and not in looking at them as transvestite males. For that reason, I dislike it when a transvestite performer suddenly removes his wig or falsies at the end of the act, as I have sometimes seen it done. If this happens, it shatters not only my illusion, but with it any erotic feeling I might have had.

It is interesting that this professional woman, when being perfectly honest, could even for a moment envy the burlesque dancer and admit that she would find it most exciting to arouse a male audience! Still, her wishful fantasy is quite sound psychologically. Women, as we have seen, do derive considerable erotic pleasure from being looked at by men, and the profession of the dancer is therefore an ideal one for exhibitionistic gratification. As our Female Psychoanalyst put it, "If the man looks at her, the woman gets excited through his looking at her."

When our Sexual Sophisticate says that she enjoys transvestite type burlesque, but reacts to the transvestite men as if they were women, she is expressing a female majority reaction. Most women do respond to such shows in just that way. Only a few women are erotically excited by the idea of men appearing in women's clothing or of exchanging sex roles with women, but *those who do* seem to derive a great deal of gratification from watching or participating in such activities. We have interviewed a small number of women who fall into this category. They were all highly intelligent, strong-willed females with decided *bi-sexual tastes* who not only liked to dress up their lovers in the underwear and outer garments of the opposite sex, but who enjoyed all kinds of masquerade for themselves.

As we have seen, a large variety of mental aphrodisiacs can and do have a powerful erotic effect on a considerable proportion of women.

As far as pornography is concerned, it is likely that many more women would respond positively to it, if it were of better quality, aesthetically less objectionable, and if it took more of the differing reactions of women into account. The *potential* or *capacity* of women to respond to psychological sex stimuli is, however, in our opinion, at least as great as that of men. If this is not fully evident at this time in our Western society, this may be due to the social conditioning of women *not* to respond to such stimuli, rather than to any innate sex differences.

On the other hand, we would not expect women to react in general to the identical stimuli to which men are known to react. On the contrary: one may be sure that men and women react *selectively* to individual aspects of the erotic object or situation, and it is in this selectivity that we must be prepared to find genuine psychological sex differences within a given society.

But women, in their own interests, need to emerge from the artificial shelters, designed to protect them from the "shocking," the "vulgar," and the "obscene," for it is axiomatic that shelters, too long lived in, breed ignorance and themselves become noisome with the miasma of false shame, prudery, and prejudice. Added to this is the well-known fact that women who have been exposed to various erotica and who can share with their male partners an interest in and enjoyment of those mental aphrodisiacs of visual or literary nature that are not contrary to their aesthetic taste and moral sensitivities, thereby contribute to a that much fuller sexual relationship with their mates.

PART III

XIII

Are Women "Touch Animals"?

In the opinion of most women, there is a distinct separation in their reactions to touch and being touched and their response to the visual stimulus of the man's body, dressed or undressed.

The connection between these two types of response is clearly demonstrated in the statements of the Female Psychoanalyst:

THE FEMALE PSYCHOANALYST

Most women don't get sexually excited by looking at a man, naked or otherwise. Obviously, a man reacts very strongly. But women need the feelings of being loved, or being touched.

I don't think the looks of a man do more than just attract her emotionally or mentally to the point where she is telling herself, "this would be a nice man to be with." And then, if he looks at her, she gets excited through his looking at her. But I don't think a woman would think, "Oh, he has beautiful legs, or he has a lovely tummy." I don't think these things excite a woman to the extent that a man can be excited by them. I have only heard women speak of a man's body or some part of his body feeling such and such, because *the tactile sense plays such a big role in women.*

The only other thing I've heard women talk about is the man's penis. Women who have had a lot of experience may say, "his was very big," or, "his was very strong," or "his was very weak looking." Even then it is more a judgment than an erotic thing, and I would say it is more in feeling the penis, or having it inside that it excites, but not just in seeing it.

Our Female Analyst's observations summarize well what is often thought about these aspects of woman's sex response, both by the professional investigator and by the layman. Yet, we cannot accept them without certain serious reservations. We shall, therefore, compare them critically with the relevant statements by our other informants to ascertain to what extent they agree or diverge from those of the Female Analyst.

In this attempt at further clarification of one of the most obscure aspects of the female sex response, we shall begin by considering women's reactions to the *sight* of the male body, before proceeding to the discussion of women's response to *touching* and *being touched*.

As to women's interest in the active observation of the human (and particularly the male) form, there can be little doubt; just as it is undeniable that women (at least women in our culture) tend to eroticize the *symbolic* aspects of masculinity (power, status, wealth, skill, intelligence, etc.) over and above the physical factors of build and beauty. While this is understood, we shall try to demonstrate by the testimony of some of our informants that the visualization of the actual physical male form does play a much larger role in the eroticism of the sexually responsive woman than has hitherto been generally recognized.

THE SEXUAL SOPHISTICATE

The Sexual Sophisticate, for instance, told us that a certain homo-erotic film short, emphasizing the male form, did have a definitely erotic appeal for her:

> The only thing that I found erotically stimulating in this film were certain sequences which showed some of the men in the most *tightly fitting sailor pants* I have ever seen. As I found

myself getting excited over some of these scenes, I began to understand why women have traditionally followed the sailor! Since then, I have often wondered how sailors got any work done in uniforms that are so tightly fitted around the buttocks and genitals that they cannot help but be confining as well as sexually stimulating to the wearer.

Even before I saw this film, I have often found my gaze being attracted to these areas when seeing sailors sauntering down the street, and I am sure that I am not the only woman who has had this experience. I can only compare it to seeing male ballet dancers in their tights, a sight which has also never failed to have a strong erotic effect on me.

On the other hand, as an interesting afterthought, she added:

On the beach, I would prefer to see men in the nude, instead of in binding, tight bikinis, as I do not like to visualize a man's penis bound and pressed down.

This, for her, seemed to suggest that the man was symbolically castrated and made into a neuter.

THE DOCTOR'S WIFE

A similar reaction to the male figure was expressed by the Doctor's Wife. Asked whether the sight of the male body and the male sex organs were able to excite her, she emphatically replied:

Sure; men often have the habit of sitting with their legs apart, and I find this very stimulating. For instance, when my husband is sitting at a bar stool with his legs apart, I think this is a very suggestive pose, even if our knees are not touching.

In another connection, the same woman told of being stimulated by the *back view* of a man, wearing tight trousers and resembling her husband in build.

It is revealing that our informant made a special point of

the fact that it was *not* necessary for her and her husband's bodies to *touch* in order for her to be sexually aroused. In fact, it seemed as if that couple had devised their own stimulation techniques of looks, words, and gestures which were fully sufficient to sexually arouse both of them, even *at some distance* from one another.

About her reactions to the male nude, the Doctor's Wife also said:

> I've watched my husband go around nude—he likes to walk about the house nude—and that stimulates me. Actually, I think I could enjoy a kind of burlesque where men would strip instead of women. . . .

The similarity between her reactions to male nudity and those of the Sexual Sophisticate is very striking, but they are even more pronounced with regard to the male genitals; said the Doctor's Wife:

> I find the penis very attractive, contrary to what I've heard some women say who find it repulsive.

Asked whether she found the looks of the flaccid or erect penis more stimulating, she replied:

> I think it is about equal, because I can imagine the limp penis becoming *erect. . . .*

THE SEXUAL SOPHISTICATE

Equally positive about the male genitals and interested in their sight, the Sexual Sophisticate said:

> I find it hard to understand that some women violently dislike the male genitals. I have noticed that I find circumcized penises aesthetically more pleasing than uncircumcized ones, because I like to see the glans and tip of the penis.
> With respect to the size of the male genitals, I seem to feel differently to what I hear from some women. I do not like the

sight of an overly large penis, nor do I appreciate an unusually small one. The same holds true for the testicles where again I prefer the golden mean, but dislike excessively large and heavy ones.

Questioned as to whether she reacted differently to the flaccid or the erect penis, she replied:

I would say, seeing the erect penis is sexually more exciting, but I don't think it's aesthetically as pleasing as the penis in the normal state. The erection somehow seems to break the harmony of the nude body, seen as a whole.

THE MARRIED LESBIAN

We had an interesting reaction to the same question from our Married Lesbian who said:

If you ask me whether I find the erect or limp penis more exciting, I'd definitely say, the *erect*. . . . But I think it interests me much more when the man is dressed than when he's undressed. I can remember feeling very attracted seeing a man fully clothed—I mean while necking—just on the point of becoming erect.

From these examples we see that women can and do react to seeing the male body and genitals, though probably not quite as strongly as men's reactions to the female form. This difference may be largely due to the greater familiarity of women with the man's body which lessens the attraction of that which is no longer hidden and taboo, but more or less openly displayed. On the other hand, the nude female form which remains normally more covered, retains its full erotic charge for the man.

In addition, female *fashions* are designed to heighten the erotic effect of certain body zones (buttocks, breasts, legs) which do have special erotic significance in our culture. There have been times in our own history when the plumage of the male was fully as important as that of the female in terms of sexual stimulation; witness the eras of tights, the well-turned leg and notably the cod-piece. Today's male fashions, however, generally do not make such appeal, but where and when they do, women can, as we have seen, react to it strongly and directly.

Further evidence for this explanation of the different reactions of men and women to the sight of the human body comes from situations in which complete nudity of both sexes is made a commonplace, such as in nudist colonies. Wherever men or women are exposed to prolonged experiences of this type, interest in the sight of the nude form decreases equally until near zero for both sexes.

Logically enough, in the nudist setting, *partial dress* becomes again the more provocative stimulus. Also, certain deliberately erotic gestures, postures, and movements will still provoke an erotic response in both men and women who are otherwise inured to the nude form.

The operation of the taboo is also well illustrated where normal interest in erotic subjects and the nude form takes on more extreme proportions, such as in the various manifestations of *voyeurism*. It is clinically well known that voyeurism in our type of society is presently almost exclusively confined to the male. How this particular obsession develops directly from the operation of the taboo on the female body has been very convincingly described in a recent Japanese novel, *The Key*.

In this extraordinary piece of literature, the author tells of a middle-aged Japanese couple and their sexual problems. The wife in this story has been brought up in the traditional Japanese way which—from their own earlier Victorian period onward—emphasized a degree of modesty which is today almost unknown in the West. The wife's refusal to let the husband see her totally in the nude leads step by step to his complete obsession with her body. (This modesty is paradoxically paired in the Japanese culture with a seemingly contradictory attitude toward nudity *in specified places* and under *special conditions,* such as in the communal bi-sexual bath).

It is clear from these examples that active *seeing* or *watching* is important to women, but undoubtedly *less* so than for (contemporary Western, or for instance, Japanese) men. We feel certain, however, that this too is a learned, or conditioned response in women. This impression is strengthened by the fact that in the past, when the taboo on male nudity was almost as strong as that on the female body, it seems that women used to show a proportionately greater interest in male anatomy.

On the other hand, the passive form of *being seen* or *watched* acts under present conditions in our society undeniably as a stronger erotic stimulus to women than to men.

With these comparisons of women's and men's reactions to the sight of the human form and women's reactions to being seen, we are now better prepared to return to the problem of women's attitudes toward touching and being touched.

If we hadn't known it before, Kinsey's studies showed conclusively that the male of the human species starts purring on being stroked just as readily as the female. More scientifically put, men have as many and as individually varied pleasure zones as women and can derive just as much erotic stimulation from them. Equally, there is no question that the sense of touch does play an important role in the love life of women, not because women are made differently, but because our culture *encourages* this response in women, while *discouraging* it in the case of men.

THE SEXUAL SOPHISTICATE

What did the women in our study think about the matter? Our Sexual Sophisticate for instance, made the following statements about the significance for her of being touched:

There is no doubt in my mind that my *clitoris* and *breasts* are the most sensitive areas of my body. But other areas do become more sensitized depending on how one touches them. I remember becoming *intensely excited* to such a degree that I could hardly tolerate the sensation, just by having a person sensuously rub his hands up and down my thighs and legs. I can also become sexually aroused by having someone brush my hair or massage my head. But the sensation from having my hair brushed or my scalp massaged is different from the one I experience from having my skin lightly caressed, in that the former is a more lazy or hypnotic kind of sensuality than an intense excitement.

Whenever any area of my body is handled in a sensuous way, I immediately begin to *respond in my genitals*. One feels a form of tension, sometimes like a pleasurable ache, or an itching that one feels can only be allayed by rubbing, instead of by scratching as other body itches seem to demand. Nibbling on the ear lobes or running the tongue over other areas of the body are also definitely sexually titillating to me. I have never failed to respond to sensuous and prolonged *tongue kissing* and for me *it is by all odds one of the most effective types of erotic stimulation*.

There is no need to go further into our informant's description of her personal reactions to the stimulation of various body zones outside of stating that her preferences—the *nipples*, *breasts* and *clitoris*—are those areas listed by the majority of women as their most sensitive pleasure spots (though a sizable proportion of women are indifferent to breast stimulation, and some even antagonistic toward it).

Beyond that, individual preferences dominate the scene with regard to different body areas which women find the most sensitive. The neck, the feet, the buttocks, the inside of the thighs, are favorites with many women, topped only by *tongue kissing*, which was also rated highly by our Sexual Sophisticate.

Perhaps the most interesting response which we received from any of our informants with regard to the problems of women's feelings about touching and being touched came from our Doctor's Wife. She described a rather unusual individual sex practice which gives us excellent insight into the erotic response potential of women with regard to touch:

> There's another thing I believe you should know. One of the things I find very stimulating and my husband does also is when we are both entirely nude and I start rubbing my face and hair all over his body and his genitals. It becomes a *hypnotizing thing*. It's *animalistic*. . . . I've watched our cat many times when she's in heat rolling over and over on the rug . . . I feel somewhat similar to what I imagine the cat feels when she's doing this. . . . There are other little animalistic things which I might do when I really get excited, like biting and scratching, and this seems to excite him too.

When reading accounts like these of women enjoying the most primitive forms of body contact, one becomes inclined to accept the notion that women are indeed touch animals. But we must not forget that this is the same woman who gave us examples showing how strongly she reacted to *words*, *sights*, and a number of other psychological aphrodisiacs which have nothing to do with the sense of touch.

In a special category belong the statements dealing with the touch of the penis against various parts of the body. The More-Than-Average Housewife made specific reference to this in the following part of her sex history:

> I love a man to walk up behind me, but I don't know why. It excites me even more, if he touches me like that with his hard penis or if he's hard against my thigh, or tummy, or sex.

This statement should be compared to a remark by the Sexual Sophisticate made in another context; she said she was stimulated by the feeling of her tongue against the glans of the penis.

Both women's comments about the man's genitals also bring to mind an ancient Chinese manuscript. That strange and rare document summarizes the whole problem of women's feelings about the penis better and more sagely than we have seen it done anywhere else. It tells of the Emperor and The Plain Girl pondering over this timeless problem with typically Oriental scholarliness and impersonal objectivity:

> The Emperor asked, "How do the various sizes and degrees of hardness of the penis affect the pleasure a woman derives from it?"
>
> The Plain Girl replied: "The size and degree of hardness with which nature has endowed a man are the outer aspect of his person. The man's ability to make it cause the woman pleasure during the act, depends on the inner aspect of his being. If the man knows how to attach the woman to him by his love and devotion, and if he impresses her with his genuine passion, she will not care whether his member is large or short, thin or thick."
>
> The Emperor asked: "What is the difference between hard and soft members?"
>
> The Plain Girl replied: "A long and thick member which is also weak and soft is inferior to one that is short and thin, but also strong and hard. On the other hand, a strong and hard member that is pushed in and out roughly is inferior to one that is soft, but moved delicately." The Golden Mean! That is the very best.

If we compare this example of Oriental wisdom with the statements of our American informants we see East and West arriving at the same conclusion. Both agree that the normal and sexually responsive woman has a positive attitude toward the man's penis; she likes to see it, hold it, and feel it inside her, and enjoys physical contact with it.

Returning now to our initial question whether women are touch animals, we must concede that for Kinsey's two-thirds majority of women who failed to respond positively to psychological sex stimuli, about the only source of erotic stimulation left is that of direct physical touch. However, one can hardly consider this the sign of an irreversible sex difference, when fully one-third of the women in the same group *did* respond to psychological sex stimuli similarly to men, and when a small percentage of them even outdid the males in this respect.

After all, the response to psychological sex stimuli is *learned* or acquired, and experience has shown that women who initially did not respond to such stimuli came to appreciate them over time, if the emotional climate and social circumstances were favorable to such changes.

The important thing to remember is that for the love life of the human animal, male or female, *all five senses* play an important role. For one individual, it may be the sense of sight, for another the sense of touch, for a third the sense of smell which is the most important. But *all of this is more a matter of individual differences than of a distinction between the two sexes.*

XIV

Lesbian Love

Among the women whom we interviewed, some had had Lesbian contacts and several of them were exclusive Lesbians. Most interesting psychologically is the woman who, like our Married Lesbian, has a predominantly Lesbian predisposition, but is trying to lead a normal marriage and family life.

Why do these women who are essentially Lesbian get married and, often enough, have children? For a variety of reasons: the desire to be like other women; the social pressures to conform and the anxiety of being left behind ("One by one my colleagues at my job left to get married," writes a married Lesbian from England*); the wish to "cure" themselves of their sexual preference for women ("Marriage, I thought to myself," says the same woman, a housewife and mother of two children, "is what I need to cure myself of my inversion and make myself normal like everybody else. . . . A husband would soon help me to overcome my natural feelings for my own sex. . . ."); sometimes just a desire to have and raise a child ("I have always wanted a child" says the Lesbian painter in her studio, proudly showing off her four-weeks-old baby girl). All of these and other factors enter into the complicated motivation of the married Lesbian.

* As quoted in "The Ladder," monthly publication of *The Daughters of Bilitis*, a national (Lesbian) organization.

The Married Lesbian

Our own Married Lesbian on whose sex history we have been drawing throughout this study, frankly told us that one of the main reasons for her getting married was the stigma our society attaches to the single woman. Asked directly about her sexual preference, our Married Lesbian did not hesitate for a moment to say, "If you give me a choice, I prefer to think of having sex with a woman every time, rather than having it with a man." As we recall, even her erotic dreams and her fantasies during intercourse with her husband showed this decided preference for her own sex.

How did this tendency of hers develop? She tells us:

> When I was thirteen, I lived in a boarding school for a while. In the first school where I lived, I had a wild, a mad crush on a totally unresponsive woman teacher. Then I changed schools and went to another school where it was the policy of the place to not only allow, but to encourage this sort of thing.
>
> I have very tender memories of this school—each of us girls was fixed on one specific woman teacher. I remember having special permission to study together with my particular teacher. So, we would go and closet ourselves in a private library and kiss and neck for hours.
>
> Of course, we only kissed on the mouth and ears, and I could never get very far beyond that. I've often wondered what would have happened, if I had really tried to go any further.
>
> I stayed at that school for two years, and they were the happiest years of my life. I've never had a better time. I was completely happy; I adored it; loved the life, the feelings, the peace . . . it was a real haven.

Undoubtedly, these highly erotically toned relationships of this woman during her impressionable pre-adolescent years were a powerful factor in tipping the balance of her sexual preference toward women. But we know from her own sex history that there had been a strong latent Lesbian tradition among the women in her family. We are therefore inclined to think that her earliest anti-male conditioning was due to the influence of her mother, grandmother, and aunts, all of whom, as she said, "considered men as their natural enemies."

As we were taking this woman's sex history, she told of a number of extremely unhappy affairs with several men, each leaving her more and more disillusioned and bitter, until she switched her erotic interests to members of her own sex.

And then I discovered women! I was studying dancing at the time. The pianist was a homosexual. He introduced me to a girl who was living with another girl. I don't think he did this with deliberation, though he might have sensed some compatibility.

She came to see me once, and I fell in love with her. In fact, I fell in love with Anne before I even saw her. This pianist had taken me and some other people to her house. While we were waiting for her, I saw her picture on the desk. I was completely fascinated by it. Then she came into the room and she was just like this picture, and that was it.

At that time, I was about nineteen and she twenty-three. I remember she was a real case. She had such a horror of men. She never expressed it, but I know that she had this terrible fear or dread of men.

It was impossible to insert a finger into her! She was just padlocked. You couldn't have pried your way in there. Once, I think, I got my finger inside of her. It was terribly painful for her. She tried to enjoy it. I was really sympathetic about this, I must say. But I realized that she was much more extreme in her feelings about men than I. Yet she was very friendly, and men were crazy about her. She had been practicing mutual masturbation with other girls since she was ten years old, and had become an active Lesbian at sixteen.

The difference in degree of Lesbian feeling and actual experience between the two women accounted for the type of sexual relationship which they had at the beginning of their affair.

The following portion of our interview with the Married Lesbian illustrates this point:

> *Question:* What did your sex with your Lesbian friend consist of?
> *Answer:* Manual first. Later, Anne and I performed cunnilingus on each other . . . rarely 69.
> *Question:* Did your lesbian friend wait to have orgasm, until you had achieved it?
> *Answer:* Why should she be so generous . . . ? No, you're right, in a sense, because it took me about two weeks until I got interested in making love to her. . . . She was a born tutor. As far as I know, she didn't care that I didn't make love to her to begin with.
> When she first started making love to me manually, I wasn't very excited. I enjoyed it. When you have never had an orgasm, you don't know what you're missing. It was very pleasant, but didn't rise or fall. After two weeks of that, I finally had my first orgasm.
> *Question:* Did she have orgasm?
> *Answer:* She had no trouble with orgasm.
> *Question:* How often did you have sex together?
> *Answer:* Well, when we first started living together and everything was very honeymoonish between us, I'd say it was every day. Still earlier, when we met secretly, it would go on for hours. . . . But toward the end, we had sex two or three times a week.

Starting with the last statement of our Married Lesbian, we note that the rate of her sexual activities with her Lesbian friend was considerably higher than that with some of her male lovers, and especially her husband with whom she admittedly had sex only at the rate of "maybe once every six weeks or so, except at those rare occasions when we were having our cyclical fights and our sex life became for the time being a thing of beauty."

These cyclical fights, she explained, had been over her husband's affair with another girl, whom in a silent kind of conspiracy, the couple had managed to introduce into their married life. Once or twice, at least, our informant told us, the three had actually gone to bed together, but these three-somes had not been very successful:

> I wasn't getting anything out of these parties. I was only doing everything for everybody else. I was the handmaiden. She refused to do anything with me. The result was, he made love to her, I made love to her, she made love to him, nobody made love to me!

What had happened was that at these occasions the wife became jealous, not so much of her husband, but of the other girl. Flatly, our informant stated: "I could have seduced her, if I had wanted to, even though my husband didn't believe it to be possible."

Why, then, did she not do it?

The answer is that if she had done so and succeeded, she would have had to play the active role and become, so to speak, the "man" in the situation. This she was not at all ready to accept, for Lesbianism had been acceptable to her in the past only when she could remain the more passive or feminine partner and let the other woman seduce her. With her husband's mistress that was out of the question, because this girl happened to be the passive, "feminine" type who was not likely to ever make the first pass at another woman, even though she too admittedly had had Lesbian relationships. Besides, if our informant had overcome her resistance and actually succeeded in seducing the other girl, she would have run the risk of losing her husband over it. As she said, "If I had to tell him the truth that would have been rather devastating to him. . . . He was so sure of her devotion to him . . . I just didn't feel like running that kind of a risk."

On the other hand, our Married Lesbian was extremely attracted to the other girl. In an autobiographical story on which she was working at the time, she tells of a visit to the other girl's apartment in which she was accompanied by her youngest child. In this literary version of her experiences, her strong erotic feelings toward her husband's mistress come through unmistakably:

> She was sitting there in the sunlight in the short orchid panties, with her beautifully muscled brown legs crossed and her elbow leaning on her knee.
>
> The baby responded readily to her caresses and as she held her arms around Yvonne's ivory neck, she pulled the short baby-doll blouse askew, baring her well-muscled chest with little breasts that stood out like twin hillocks.
>
> I recognized as in a dream all the things Bert saw in her and wanted. . . .
>
> From time to time she made a gesture as of modesty: she may have been embarrassed, sitting almost naked in front of me, and yet, as I came to know afterwards, she might have even then been showing off her body as if to say: "You can't blame him, can you?"
>
> And in me there rankled a feeling of inferiority, because I was not like Yvonne, the acrobat of the pink-padded-thigh, of the peaches-and-cream behind, the possessor of the violet-tinted nipples surrounded with a dark nimbus of hair which my husband described with a tiny shudder as "sexy."

This, of course, was admiration, envy, and jealousy speaking all at once. With such contradictory feelings on the part of our Married Lesbian one could hardly have expected any kind of relationship between the three people to work out. Still, several months after this uneasy triangle had broken up, our Married Lesbian expressed sincere regret that "this woman was out of our lives." For, as she said, while it all lasted, "each person excited the other one for the third!"

If we have dwelt on this rather unusual relationship, it is because it is highly instructive in several respects.

First of all, we have noticed that marriages similar to that of our informant are more common than is generally thought. We have already briefly referred to the English Lesbian who had imprisoned herself in an unworkable heterosexual marriage and who felt, as she said elsewhere, that she should warn others in her predicament that marriage is not the cure for inversion.

The Lesbian tendency was perhaps stronger in the British woman than in the case of our Married Lesbian. Yet, her most satisfactory sexual relations had been with women and not with men, and the motives for her getting married were, as we have seen, rather dubious. In fact, she told us, the most decisive but totally accidental factor in her getting married was that her father, with whom she had been living at the time, was going on an extended trip and wanted to close up the house!

Another important factor to consider is our Married Lesbian's ambivalence or mixed feelings about Lesbian love itself! She could never really make up her mind (and that in spite of considerable psychoanalytic therapy) whether she liked women better than men, or vice versa. This might have been due to a prejudice in the analysis itself and a perhaps too dominant desire on the part of her analyst to direct her sexual energies into heterosexual channels. We do not know. What we do know is that she never succeeded in fully resolving this problem in her own mind. If she could have made such a decision, she might have made a much better adjustment, either in a heterosexual or in a Lesbian way. The worst and most neurotic thing about her sex life was that she could not fully accept and enjoy either the one or the other type of relationship.

THE SEXUAL SOPHISTICATE

Of the other women in our study on whose sex histories we are drawing most heavily for our discussion, only the Sexual Sophisticate had had any personal experience with Lesbian love, and that without letting it interfere, in any way, with her predominantly heterosexual predisposition. Since her account of these sex contacts is, as usual, comparatively perceptive and specific with regard to her own response to these experiences, we shall here present one of them, just as she related it to us:

> My one and only Lesbian experience was with a friend of mine, slightly older than myself, whom I found physically attractive.
> We started out kissing and fondling each other's breasts which was exciting to both of us. After we had been enjoying this for a while, my friend who was sitting on the bed, placed me across her knees while supporting me with one arm under my shoulders. In this way she was able to kiss me and fondle my breast with one hand while masturbating me with the other free hand, and it was not long until I felt myself having my first Lesbian orgasm in her arms.
> We then changed positions, both of us lying down on the bed, my friend performing cunnilingus on me, while I was masturbating her manually. Again, I had orgasm in this way and my friend as well.
> It was a good arrangement, because I don't like to perform cunnilingus, while my friend liked it, but did not insist on having it done to her. However, I don't think I would ever make a good Lesbian, for I would think that one would have to enjoy performing cunnilingus to make a real success of it.
> In some of the pornographic books I have read, I have come across descriptions of women making love to each other with dildoes. This idea of women wearing artificial penises doesn't interest me sexually in the least. I just think they look ridiculous and would not enjoy having one used on me. The only things I could imagine myself doing with another woman are those I did and had done to me at this one occasion.

In the statement by our Sexual Sophisticate the most conspicuous feature is, by its very absence, any sense of guilt about her Lesbian contact. She tells about it with the same naturalness and serious, but casual objectivity with which we have already heard her comment on other aspects of her sexual behavior, whether socially acceptable or not.

In this instance she seems fully to bear out a contention by Prof. Kinsey which is fully supported by our own observations, that every individual has the inherent capacity to respond to either heterosexual or homosexual stimulation, "if the opportunity was offered and one were not conditioned against making such responses."

Nowhere else is this plasticity of the human psyche to respond to a variety of sexual stimuli better illustrated than in the erotic literature of continental Europe in the eighteenth century. During that period, the social atmosphere toward deviant sexual behavior and especially toward Lesbian love was much more tolerant than it has been ever since anywhere in the Western world. Consequently, one finds in the literature of that time an almost casual shifting from Lesbianism to heterosexual behavior, and vice versa, without undue guilt reactions and the kind of emotional strain which generally accompany such behavior today.

CASANOVA AND LESBIAN LOVE

Taking only one among many such references to mixed sexual activities in Casanove de Seingalt's famous *Memoirs*, we find him on this occasion involved with a girl by the name of Marcoline who had a decided Lesbian preference and another girl whom he calls Irene:

> "Come! let us to bed!" said she [Marcoline], and after taking off her clothes she helped Irene to undress. I had no wish to fight against two, and said that I wanted to rest. The fair Venetian burst out laughing and said: "Go to bed and leave us alone!"
>
> I did so, and amused myself watching the two Bacchantes; but Irene, who had evidently never engaged in such a combat before, was not nearly so adroit as Marcoline.
>
> Before long Marcoline brought Irene in her arms to my bedside, and told me to kiss her.
>
> "Leave me alone, dearest," said I, "the punch has got into your head, and you don't know what you are doing."
>
> This stung her; and urging Irene to follow her example, she took up a position in my bed by force; and as there was not enough room for three, Marcoline got on top of Irene, calling her her wife. I was virtuous enough to remain a wholly passive

spectator of the scene, which was always new to me, though I had seen it so often; but at last they flung themselves on me with such violence that I was obliged to give way, and for the most part of the night I performed my share of the work, till they saw that I was completely exhausted. We fell asleep, and I did not wake up till noon, and then I saw my two beauties still asleep, with their limbs interlaced like the branches of a tree. I thought with a sigh of the pleasures of such a sleep, and got out of bed gently for fear of arousing them.

When I came back I found my two Lesbians awake, and they gave me such an amorous welcome that I felt inclined to complete the work of the night with a lover's good morning; but I began to feel the need of husbanding my forces, so I did nothing, and bore their sarcasms in silence. . . .

"We have enjoyed ourselves," said Marcoline, "and time that is given to enjoyment is never lost."

It seems that Casanova was agreed with Marcoline's hedonistic philosophy of pleasure as stated by her at the end of the quotation. His tolerance toward Lesbianism was, of course, made easy by his voyeuristic interests in such activities and was able to override in the long run any feelings of hurt masculine pride which he sometimes expressed in similar situations.

This voyeuristic interest in Lesbian activities on the part of men is well known and may account in part for the relatively greater social tolerance of Lesbianism as against that shown toward male homosexuality. It seems as though men are inclined to take Lesbian love not quite so seriously as homosexual behavior, but mentally transform it into a heterosexual situation by projecting themselves into it. In addition, Lesbian love poses no threat to any possible latent homosexuality within themselves.

Frank Harris and Lesbian Love

An almost identical attitude to that of Casanova with regard to Lesbian love was shown by the British writer Frank Harris. Like Casanova he saw nothing wrong in the oc-

casional Lesbian experiences of his girl friends and regarded
them as mere trifles, especially if they concerned the past
and not the present. On the other hand, the nineteenth century women who told him about their previous Lesbian
contacts were far from being as care- and guilt-free about
them as the Lesbians or bi-sexuals that Casanova is talking
about.

At one point in his memoirs (*My Life and Loves*), Harris
tells of a young woman who first confessed to him how much
she had enjoyed her previous Lesbian relationships and who
then complained about having been encouraged in this way
by other girls.

Harris wrote:

> "Why shouldn't you be encouraged?" I couldn't help asking.
> "I was already too much inclined that way," she replied.
> "So much the better," I went on; "I can't understand the
> implied condemnation."
> "Nor can I," she rejoined. "It's merely habit, the customary
> way of thinking and speaking."

This quotation from Frank Harris' autobiography clearly
shows the guilt-producing effect of prevailing social attitudes
about deviant sex behavior in the community. The girl in
this instance felt guilty only because she had blindly taken
over and accepted the dominant cultural attitudes and not, as
it transpired in answer to Harris' questions, because she had
arrived at any *personal* conviction on the matter by her own
thought-processes.

There are, of course, many women of stronger character
who do overcome the social pressures to conform to the
generally accepted standards of sexual behavior. Among this
group belong undoubtedly a great number of those for whom
Lesbian love has indeed become a way of life and who cannot or will not change their preference for their own sex:
"It seems to be almost a law," one Lesbian woman wrote to
Frank Harris, "that we love those who respond to us and

worship all that gives us pleasure in its very widest sense. Vice—! The thought amuses me. There are only vicious people."

THE CONFIRMED LESBIAN

Still deeper insights into the psychology of Lesbian love can be gained from one of the most interesting auto-biographical documents of a confirmed Lesbian which has come to our attention. We are referring to the untranslated autobiography of an Austrian woman (Edith Cadivec), whose English title would be *Eros—The Meaning of My Life*. In this book (*Eros, der Sinn meines Lesbens*, privately published in 1930), the Lesbian author describes her passionate love for another woman by the name of Senta with whom she had had a long affair.

We have translated, and will quote from a passage which is important not only for a better understanding of Lesbian love, but even more so for our comprehension of the nature and intensity of the feelings which may characterize these relationships.

The passage tells of an experience which took place during the period when the love between the two women was undergoing a severe crisis and the rift between them was already quite evident. In this emotional setting, the author gives us an extraordinarily well-drawn picture of the two lovers' last efforts to rekindle the already dying flame of their love into the white-hot blaze of former passion:

> As in a dream I embrace Senta's body with affectionate arms, lift it up and carry it triumphantly to my bed. . . . I undress and step to her at the bed. With a loving gesture I bend deep down and whisper her name into her ear.
> "Senta! . . . Darling! . . ."
> My face which I offer her touches her burning cheeks, my breath intermingles with hers. . . . With a passionate movement she throws her arms around my neck and takes a hold

of my head. At once Senta's hot lips attach themselves to mine —hot, sensuous, like an animal in heat. . . .

I feel the thrill of sexual excitement . . . seconds of dizziness cloud my consciousness. . . .

I disengage myself from her clutching embrace, tear myself away, and cover Senta's whole body with glowing kisses. The sweet scent of her feminine sensuality bewitches my senses. . . . My intoxicated mouth begins the game of supreme delight with tender kisses. . . .

Senta calls my name, sighing and stammering . . . her body melts into my body, her soul into my soul. . . . My arms keep the overflowing cup of delight pressed tightly to my lips . . . my trembling hands reach for the delicious buds of her breasts and press them lightly between my affectionate hands. . . .

Senta screams, writhes, and calls me by name. . . . She is raging like one delirious. . . .

My lips, my tongue greedily sip the nectar of bliss . . . they feel the quivering of the nerves, the spasms of ecstasy. . . . They know exactly when it is time to linger at the point of supreme delight. . . . Suddenly, her body convulsively raises up beneath me as a long drawn-out scream of ecstasy makes the room tremble; in the most intense climax her whole body quakes and shivers with delight. . . . And I collapse over my sweetheart's body which convulses in the spasms of orgasm and float away—united with her—into the happy paradise of Eros. . . .

If the above quoted excerpt from the Lesbian autobiography conveys, as we have pointed out, the intensity of passionate feelings that are frequently part and parcel of Lesbian relationships, it is also indicative of the effectiveness of Lesbian love techniques. This is, indeed, so much the general experience that Kinsey was forced to adjust his incidence figures of the female orgasm to account for the fact that many of the women in his sample *regularly* achieved *multiple* orgasm in their Lesbian, though not necessarily in their heterosexual relations. He accounts for this by observing, "Two individuals of the same sex are likely to understand the anatomy and the physiologic responses and psychology of their own sex better than they understand that of the opposite sex," an explanation which becomes all the more understandable in the light of our discussion under "The Anatomy of Orgasm."

Yet, it is necessary to weigh these apparent advantages in Lesbian love against the possible inherent disadvantages in such relationships, if one wants to arrive at an unbiased appraisal of woman's love for woman.

In the first place, one has to differentiate between the woman who can accept and enjoy an occasional Lesbian experience and the confirmed and exclusive Lesbian who does not respond to heterosexual stimulation at all.

THE FEMALE PSYCHOANALYST

The same female psychoanalyst whose opinions on other aspects of female sexuality we have already considered in various parts of our study drew this line of demarcation very clearly and explained that as far as she herself was concerned, she could accept the milder, but not the more pronounced forms of Lesbianism:

> As a variation I can theoretically accept Lesbianism and I can image somebody enjoying it as a kind of sex play but as a way of life I think it is deplorable.
>
> I realize that for some women and some men it may be the best possible adjustment. But personally I would always be unhappy about it, because I do feel that *biologically* speaking it is just not as satisfactory as the real deal. It's like a hole and a peg, they belong together and two holes and two pegs just don't match, it's as simple as that.
>
> I also think the psychological relationship between two men or two women is different in a way from the heterosexual relationship. . . . Competition and the Oedipal situation enter into it and make it different. Anyway, biologically and psychologically, I can see homosexuality as a game but not as a way of life.

We can follow the female psychoanalyst's reasoning on homosexuality and Lesbianism to a certain point. We also are

inclined to think that *exclusive* (Lesbian or male) homosexuality constitutes an unnecessary and possibly unhealthy
limitation. However, by the same reasoning, might one not
have to apply the same standard to an exclusively heterosexual orientation?

All we actually know is that Kinsey and his co-workers
found that the group of individuals in their sample who had
had a considerable amount of homosexual contact seemed
neither more nor less disturbed emotionally than the rest of
the population. Said Kinsey, " . . . interpretations of homosexuality as neurotic or psychopathic behavior or moral de-
generacy, and other philosophical interpretations are not
supported by scientific research, and are contrary to the
specific data on our series of female and male histories."

From our own experience and research we can only say
that in general our observations coincide with those of Kinsey
and his co-workers, provided one makes due allowance for the
effects of the social pressures which are still brought to bear
upon the homosexual or Lesbian in our society. These social
pressures must make some kind of impact on the affected
person just as they affect other groups of deviants from the
cultural norm.

However, some studies seem to indicate that Lesbians as a
group may be better adjusted socially than male homosexuals.
We would account for this on the basis that the social pressures affecting the male homosexual are generally more
severe than those to be tolerated by the Lesbian in our
society.

To minimize these social pressures and give the Lesbian
or male homosexual an equal chance of integration and
happiness, we are emphatically in support of all such efforts
as the Wolfenden proposals in England which would legalize
homosexual contacts between consenting adults. Until such
recommendations have been adopted and have been observed
in practice, we think it would be impossible to evaluate correctly what effect, if any, homosexual or Lesbian disposition

may have on the character-formation and mental health of the individual.

We may find that sexual orientation has a great deal to do with individual mental health and personal happiness. But we may also find that sexual preference *per se* has little or nothing to do with general emotional well-being or disturbance.

PART IV

XV

The Future of Female Sexuality

W<small>HAT</small> the future may hold one can only deduce from what the present foreshadows, in sex as in any other form of human activity.

A recent case in England exemplifies the present and indicates the trend of tomorrow. A female student at Oxford was expelled because she had been found in bed with a man, also an Oxford student. What is significant is that other college girls were especially aggrieved that the young man who had taken part in the act had been suspended for only ten days, and was not subjected to the harsh discipline meted out to the female offender.

One of the girl's fellow-students was quoted by the press as saying of the affair: "It smacked of sheer Victorian melodrama. We are all furious at the unequal treatment meted out to the girl and the man. I think a girl's sex-life is her own business."

The case should cheer Simone de Beauvoir in Paris, as she has long been depressed by women's *lack of solidarity* with their own cause. "They live dispersed," she said, "among the males, attached through residence, housework, economic conditions, and social standing to certain men—fathers or husbands—more firmly than they are to other women. If they belong to the bourgeoisie, they feel solidarity with men of that class, not with proletarian women; if they are white, their allegiance is to white men, not to Negro women."

If women are not becoming more united in the fight for their sexual and other interests, all indications are that they are at least becoming sexually more alive, sophisticated, and demanding. Also, they are getting bolder in their approach and less willing to wait for the man to make the first move. One of our informants, the Doctor's Wife, gave us a typical example of this tendency:

> Just the other day I was at an auction with a girl friend of mine and I saw a man in the crowd who resembled my husband very much in his physical proportions. He was wearing very tight trousers more from the rear than from the front. I was looking his way and smacking my lips as I was watching him and said to my girl friend "It's too bad we have to go; I rather like the scenery." She seemed a little shocked and said, "I thought only men were supposed to say things like that!"

In the future, we would think, nobody will be shocked at such a simple admission of sexual interest, even if displayed by a married woman, mother, and respectable member of the community.

Greater sexual aggressiveness is already no longer confined to any particular age-group or class of women. The merry widow and the divorcée who, traditionally, have been accepted as more forward, have been joined by older age-groups of women and also by very young girls who can hardly yet be called women. These young girls, whatever their initial motivation for early sex experience, are unlikely to accept the restrictions of repressive sexual codes later in life.

Yet, what modern women seem to want is not just *more* sex, but *better* sex. Together with increased aggressiveness in mature women, there appears to be a trend toward demanding, and if necessary, seeking, better sexual performance from male partners. There are also ample signs that the nature of the relationship between man and woman, husband and wife, is gradually undergoing a change.

Traditionally, and in its crudest form, woman has long been considered the sexual property of man. It is a relationship of humiliation, symbolized by the notorious chastity belt with which husbands were entitled to make sure that their property rights were secured during their physical absences.

It is amazing that not only this viewpoint, but also the practice itself was able to survive into the last decades of the nineteenth century. A prospectus, issued by a Paris firm manufacturing such girdles at prices ranging from 120 to 320 francs, reads:

> The husband will leave his wife without fear that his honor will be outraged and his affections estranged. Many discussions and shameful actions will cease. Fathers will be sure of their parenthood and will not harbor the terrible thought that their children may be the offspring of another, and it will be possible for them to keep under lock and key things more precious than gold.

How did woman behave when thus degraded into a mere sex object of the man?

As Simone de Beauvoir very correctly points out, she has had the choice of either reacting through the masculine protest, by identifying with man and behaving like one, or she could "make use of her feminine weapons to *wage war* upon the male."

On the surface it would seem that women acquiesced, submitted, even protested that they loved to be possessed, and kept in their place by men. In an age when it was difficult for a woman to achieve independence, the rewards of being the second sex were too tempting. Woman, by accepting her inferior status, acquired the privileges of the weak: the man who owned her also became responsible for her. The "little woman" was not expected to go out into the cold, cruel world and fight for a living, at least not as long as her main contribution to society was to serve the food which the male breadwinner provided, and to keep order in the nursery.

These are the secondary gains which women have at stake in the present condition of our civilization. They cannot be expected to give them up on principle alone any more than the neurotic who holds on to the indirect advantages which his emotional disturbance provides. Woman's question to her would-be liberators is thus the same as the mental patient would ask of those wishing to cure him: *"What have you got to offer* in return for the surrender of my illness?"

This threatened loss in material and emotional security adds its weight to the lack of solidarity among women and represents, we believe, the ultimate cause of women's ambivalence toward the issue of their own sexual liberation. Only when this mental block is finally removed can we therefore expect a real breakthrough on the subject of women's rights. Until then, the majority of women themselves will sabotage any serious efforts on their behalf.

Nevertheless, certain social changes are taking place today which are gradually undermining the traditional feminine notion of comfort. The young middle-class wife, living in a two- or three-room flat in town, finds the boredom of playing house under these conditions more intolerable than putting up with the inconvenience of rush-hour traffic to and from her old job. In similar manner, the young suburban housewife, and even the country-town housewife, today occupies herself with a multiplicity of activities, most of which are destined to fill up the void occasioned by the absence of full-time housekeeping activities.

In addition, more effective and convenient methods of birth control, such as the new oral contraceptives, may lead to a further reduction in the size of the modern family. When that occurs another necessity will be removed for the modern woman to stay at home much longer than the first few years, owing to lighter housekeeping duties and planned family living.

Moreover, the young wife is far more aware than her grandmother of the need for sex education with respect to her children. In attending to their needs, she may well learn more about herself. Her whole psychological horizon is expanding, and indeed the concept of psychology itself, as an exploration of the emotions, already preoccupies members of our middle and upper classes. No matter how superficial or exaggerated this may be in individual cases, it provides the right sort of climate for the freer discussion of sex problems. With increased information, with vastly speeded up methods of communication, and with greater leisure, it is thus very likely that the majority of women, even despite continued dependence on the atavistic dispensers of their "security," will begin to insist on greater freedom in sexual matters than they have previously enjoyed.

With these changes in the psychology and status of women, one is forced to ask oneself, what is the sex-life of tomorrow going to look like?

About one hundred years ago, a woman dared to make a long-range forecast of female sexuality in a pamphlet entitled, *Sex Economics on the Planet Mars*. In that now rare and forgotten little document, the female visionary has her woman from outer space explain to an earth inhabitant the mechanics of Martian sex life and sex ethics.

> "We have no wives and no husbands as you do," she quotes the Martian as saying, "consequently, we have no marriage and no divorce. No man belongs to any woman and no woman gives herself to any man for a longer period of time than what is within the limits of her own love and desire."

Just how unrealistic or far-fetched might this futuristic fantasy be? Perhaps not nearly so much as appears on first glance. In fact, we would not be at all surprised if many women of tomorrow will be doing very much the same as our Sexual Sophisticate does today—with the difference that such behavior will then be more socially acceptable.

We would think that the future sex roles of men and women will have a more similar pattern. This does not imply that women will necessarily become more masculinized and men more feminized, but that the trend will be for less pronounced social sex differences than are the rule today. In keeping with this trend, we would for instance, expect women to show as strong an interest in all kinds of psychological sex stimuli or mental aphrodisiacs in art and literature as is more typical for men today.

As this liberal development continues, orgasm ability in women will cease to be a specifically feminine problem. The woman of tomorrow will automatically expect to experience the orgastic climax to sexual relations. This, of course, will anticipate a new willingness and pride on the part of the man to evoke this kind of orgastic response in his female partner: in short, the future of female sexuality also involves changes in male sexuality. "It may be," says French playwright Jean Genet with the intuitive understanding of the true invert, "that the emancipation of the modern woman obliges the man to give up old attitudes and find a new one, more in keeping with the less submissive woman."

What are the gains and losses likely to be on either side?

For the man, these will consist mainly of a loss of face which is, however, more imagined than real. In return, he will get the kind of understanding female companion and erotically awake sex partner for which he has always yearned.

And the woman? For her, it will be mainly the loss of the male provider and protector in the more traditional sense of the terms. If she can face that, and future events may actually give her little choice in the matter, her rewards will be great and many. With her acceptance of full adult status in the community of responsible humans, she will regain her lost birthright to sexual happiness, for which neither mink coats nor bourgeois respectability are good enough substitutes.

In the past, the enormously practical adaptability of the female has enabled her to live, albeit resentfully, with the double sex standard. In so doing, woman was sacrificing her claim to sexual equality in exchange for the security of marriage that was, for her at any rate, supposedly monogamous. At present, with the double sex standard eroding rapidly, not only men, but also women, are indulging increasingly in pre-marital and extra-marital relationships. The only difference is that for women such relationships still remain burdened by more social disapproval and are therefore accompanied by stronger guilt and fear reactions than is true in the case of men.

But there is no reason why the practical adaptability of women should not be put to good use, even within the structure of monogamous marriage. Once women have accepted the full drive of their own natural sexuality, they can exercise their equally natural curiosity and ingenuity to contribute to a more diverse, exciting, and satisfying monogamous relationship, if that is what both partners prefer.

On the other hand, we would assume that in the future an ever increasing number of women will come to place less and less emphasis upon *absolute* monogamy for their sexual and emotional happiness. Here again, we believe, more and more women will over time adopt an attitude which resembles the present male point of view on these matters, especially if the threat to their economic security and the social onus are removed.

In other words, we do not believe that the woman of tomorrow will want to give up monogamy although she may then be much more alive sexually, more mature emotionally, and more independent economically. For example, we do not interpret the statements of some of our female informants, for instance those of the Sexual Sophisticate or of the More-Than-Average Housewife, to mean that they wished to do away with marriage and family life altogether. What these women desired, and what we think more women in the future will want is monogamy, but *monogamy with freedom*. However, this must be real freedom, not the false freedom man now enjoys because of the double sex standard, nor the grudging tolerance shown to modern woman who is allowed to "sin," providing she is not found out. Above all, future generations will certainly not wish a return to the old strait jacket of enforced and absolute monogamy which has proved to be temperamentally incompatible to such a large percentage of both men and women.

To repeat, we believe that what the women (and, for that matter, the men) of tomorrow will want, is monogamy with all the emotional security, intimacy and devotion which only a relatively stable relationship can provide. But, in contrast with the present, such relationships will in the future be held together by mutual desire and consent rather than by legal coercion or economic necessity. An ever increasing number of men and women, we should think, will want this kind of *flexible monogamy* which avoids hypocrisy and betrayal, but which frankly allows for variety, friendships, and even sexual experiences with other individuals, if these are desired. A monogamy in short, similar to what the Sexual Sophisticate's story anticipates, with a deep and meaningful, but not necessarily all-exclusive relationship to one person.

The future will also bring with it, we believe, an emphasis on *variety* in patterns of sexual and marital relations. This, we think, should have a very strong appeal to the more rational, scientific side of our nature. In other words, we would think that society will come to insist less that all marriages be fashioned in the same mold. And, it should be added, in this new pattern of sexual relationships with its emphasis on respect for individual differences, that form of exclusive monogamy which is still our society's official marriage ideal, will also have a place. The only difference is that monogamy will no longer be an imposition from the outside and an unbearable burden for so many people, but the result of the corresponding needs of the partners and the expression of their own free choice.

How long will these subtle changes take to become the

accepted practice of tomorrow? The question is more easily posed than answered. The old and the new order of things are engaged today in a life and death struggle on every frontier of human experience, with both elements alternating in their grasp of temporary ascendancy. The resistance of those who have emotional or economic interests in the social, and therefore also the sexual status quo, and the tenacious grip which prejudice and hide-bound moralism still exert on the modern mind will undoubtedly continue to exert their retarding influence. But we are sufficiently optimistic to anticipate that reason and a new style in human relationships, including sexual relationships, will eventually develop out of the present chaos of painful conflicts and contradictions.

To repeat: in our view, the future of female sexuality clearly points to far-reaching changes in our entire social framework. It includes precepts which, if acted upon, will fundamentally alter not only the structure of marriage and family life as we now know it, but also affect the role of women in the political and economic spheres, and vice versa. In other words, we are seeing the remaining sexual liberation of women as part of their general emancipation, and their general emancipation as part of a larger trend toward social reconstruction. Thus, sexual happiness is, to our minds, inextricably bound up with human progress and welfare in the widest sense of the terms, in which the future of female sexuality may be both the key and the barometer.

APPENDIX

The Female
Sex Response

Chart 1: External Non-Genital Anatomical Response

PHASES	LENGTH OF TIME	BREASTS
Excitement	From a few minutes to several hours, depending upon intensity, continuity and techniques of sexual stimulation (measured from onset of sexual stimulation to onset of plateau phase).	Nipple erection (increase in length 1.0 to 1.5 cm.; increase in diameter at nipple base 0.5 to 1 cm.). Areolae (colored areas around nipples) become puffy and engorged. Breast increases in size ½ to ¼ more than normal proportions. Bluish vein markings on breast become more noticeable.
Plateau	Generally of much shorter duration than the excitement phase.	Measle-like rash (vascular flush) appearing first on the lower breast surfaces.
Orgasm	From three to eight or even ten seconds. The longer the orgasm phase, the more severe the physiological and anatomical reactions.	No specific breast response. Measle-like rash reaches maximum spread.
Resolution	Roughly proportional in time sequence to the excitement phase: If short excitement phase followed in rapid succession by plateau and orgasm, resolution will be short; if lengthy excitement phase, followed only by plateau without orgasm, resolution from unrelieved sexual tension will be long and frustrating.	Return slowly to normal size (in direct reversal of excitement phase): 1) Measle-like skin rash disappears. 2) Breasts return to normal size. 3) Areolae lose engorged, swollen appearance. 4) Erect nipples return to normal state.

241

CHART 2: EXTERNAL GENITAL ANATOMICAL RESPONSE

PHASES	CLITORIS	LABIA MAJORA	LABIA MINORA	BATHOLIN'S GLANDS
Excitement	Frequently 2 to 3 times size increase. Great individual variation. (Size increase completed at the end of this phase.)	Reaction varies with numbers of children woman has borne. No-children female: labia thin out, flatten upward and backward. More-than-one-child female: increase in size 2 to 3 times of normal state. Tendency for labia to spread sideways as plateau phase is approached, making vaginal outlet available for coitus.	Increase in size 2 to 3 times normal thickness. Extend laterally to provide additional support and adds 1.0 to 1.5 cm. of coital length to the vagina. Turn bright pink in color.	Do not secrete unless excitement phase is maintained for a markedly extended time.
Plateau	No specific response.	No-children female: labia majora a non-existent entity during phase. Otherwise, no specific response.	Marked color change. No-children female: cardinal red; More-than-one-child: burgundy red. These color changes always evidence of approaching orgasm.	Onset of 3 or 4 drops of glandular secretion.
Orgasmic	No specific response.	No specific response.	No specific response. Length of time from onset of color changes during plateau phase to orgasm—60 to 90 seconds. If no orgasm occurs, the bright pink of excitement phase remains.	No specific response.
Resolution	Engorgement is lost very slowly; frequently last of pelvic sexual anatomy to return to normal size. Especially true if no orgasmic relief was achieved.	Return to normal anatomical position and size. This occurs more rapidly for the no-children female than for the more-than-one-child female.	Complete reversal from the excitement phase. First, lose discoloration, from cardinal or burgundy red to pink within 90 to 120 secs. after orgasm. From pink back to normal color not as uniform. Total color changes back to normal completed within 5 minutes. Second, return slowly to normal position and size.	Cessation of secretory activity.

242

CHART 3: INTERNAL PELVIC ANATOMICAL RESPONSE

PHASES	VAGINA	CERVIX	UTERUS	FALLOPIAN TUBES AND OVARIES
Excitement	Begins to lubricate from walls, the sweating phenomenon, within 10 to 20 secs. of onset of sexual stimulation. Lubricating material changes normal acidity of vagina. Inner two-thirds of vagina increases in depth and width. Width increase: 2 to 3 times of normal state. Length increase: 2 to 4 cms. depending on previous child-bearing experience. Vaginal walls develop darker, purplish hue.	No secretion. Pulled back and away from the vaginal outlet and upward toward the false pelvis. Occurs at same time vagina expands in width and depth.	Pulled upward into the false pelvis if uterus is in a normal (anterior) position.	As yet nothing is known about response.
Plateau	Lubrication is present in varying degree. Vaginal expansion concluded before plateau phase is reached. No further significant changes to inner two-thirds of vagina. Vaginal responses confined to external third of vagina. Entire vaginal canal is congested so that the circumference of the outer third of the vagina is constricted to ⅓ to ½ of excitement phase distension.	No secretion. No specific response.	No specific response.	As yet nothing is known about response.
Orgasmic	Lubrication is present in varying degree even if orgasm is not achieved. Vagina contracts rhythmically from 4 to 10 times with approximately 8/10 sec. between contractions. The more intense the orgasmic experience, the more noticeable the contractions.	No secretion. Immediately after orgasm, slight opening of the external cervical os.	Regular contraction sequence of the uterine wall.	As yet nothing is known about response.
Resolution	Lubrication stops. 1) Outer third of vagina shrinks back to normal size within 60 to 90 secs. 2) Inner two-thirds expansion of vaginal depth and width slowly recedes—5 to 8 minutes.	No secretion. Cervix drops down into the depth of the vagina as it loses its distension and vaginal wall loses its vascocongestion.	Return to normal uterine position as the vaginal walls collapse.	As yet nothing is known about response.

243

CHART 4: GENERAL URO-GENITAL RESPONSE

PHASES	THE PERINEUM	URETHRA AND URINARY BLADDER	RECTUM
Excitement	No specific response. Vulva turns to bright pink color.	No specific response.	No specific response.
Plateau	A spasmodic tightening of the perineal body during the end of plateau phase as orgasm is approached. More-than-one-child woman: vulva turns from bright pink to scarlet red or burgundy.	No specific response.	No specific response.
Orgasmic	Involuntary, irregular elevation of the entire perineum.	Occasional, involuntary spreading of the external meatus. Minimal reaction with no regularity nor with any direct relationship to orgasmic intensity. No involuntary loss of urine.	Active contraction of the rectal sphincter. Does not always occur. A significant indication of intensity of orgasm.
Resolution	No specific response.	No specific response.	No specific response.

Selected Bibliography

ANON. *Galante Abenteuer der Saengerin Wilhelmine* (Schroeder-Devrient). Jules Flangarin: Paris, n.d. (Numerous later reprints.)

ANON. (Tomita, K., trans.) Hikatsu-sho. Ms, typed, i + 83 p., ca. 1845.

ABRAHAM, HILDA C. "A contribution to the problem of female sexuality," *Intern. J. Psych.*, 37:351–353, 1956.

ABRAHAMSON, H. A. "Lysergic acid diethylamid (LSD 25) as an adjunct to psychotherapy with elimination of homosexuality," *J. Psychol.*, 39, 127, 1955.

ADAMS, C. R. "An informal preliminary report on some factors relating to sexual responsiveness of certain college wives," Ms, typed, mimeo., ii + 70 p., 1953.

ADLER, ALFRED. (Jensen, E. & F., trans.) *The case of Miss R.: The interpretation of a life story.* N.Y.: Greenberg, 1929.

ADLER, OTTO. *Die mangelhafte Geschlechtsempfindung des Weibes. Anaesthesia sexualis feminarum. Anaphrodisia. Dyspareunia.* Berlin: H. Kornfeld, 1911. (Traditional medical point of view, postulating the sexual inferiority of woman.)

ALLEN, CLIFFORD. "Female orgastic capacity," *J. Sexol.*, 2:187–188, 1949.

—— "The personality of Radclyffe Hall," *J. Sexol.*, 4:95–98, 1950.

ALLEN, C. N. "Recent research on sex differences," *Psych. Bull.*, 32:343–354, 1935.

American Association of Marriage Counselors. "Premarital sex relations: The facts and the counselor's role in relation to the facts." (Report of a round table meeting held by the Section on Marriage and Family Counseling of the National Council on Family Relations at Lake Geneva, Wisc., Aug. 30, 1951.) *Marr. & Fam. Liv.*, 14:229–238, 1952.

ANTHONY, REY (pseud.). *A housewife's handbook on selective promiscuity.* New York: Documentary Books, 1961.

BALINT, MICHAEL. *Problems of human pleasure and behavior.* New York: Liveright, 1957.

BARTLETT, R. G. "Physiologic responses during coitus," *J. Applied Physiol.*, 9(3):469–472, 1956.

BEAUVOIR, SIMONE DE. *Le deuxième sexe. I. Les faits et les mythes. II. L'expérience vécue.* Paris: Gallimard, 1952. (Parshley, H. M., trans.) *The second sex.* New York: Alfred A. Knopf.

BENDER, LAURETTA, and BLAU, A. "The reaction of children to sexual relations with adults," *Amer. J. Orthopsychiat.*, 7:500–518, 1937.

BENDER, LAURETTA, and CRAMER, J. B. "Sublimation and sexual gratification in the latency period of girls," in Eissler, K. R., et al., ed. *Searchlights in delinquency*, pp. 53–64, 1949.

BENEDEK, THERESE. *Psychosexual functions in women.* New York: Ronald Press, 1952.

BENEDEK, T., and RUBENSTEIN, B. B. "The sexual cycle in women." Washington, D.C.: Nat. Research Council (*Psychosom. Med. Mono., v.3, No. 1 and 2*), 1942.

BERGLER, E. "The problem of frigidity," *Psychiat. Quart.* 18:374–390, 1944. (Ultra-orthodox psychoanalytic point of view.)

—— "Lesbianism, facts and fiction," *Marr. Hyg.* 1:197–202, 1948. (See above for commentary.)

—— 1951. *Neurotic counterfeit-sex.* Impotence, frigidity, "mechanical" and pseudo-sexuality, homosexuality. New York: Grune & Stratton, 1951. (See for an extreme opposite viewpoint to that in this book.)

BERKELEY-HILL, OWEN. "The Erotic rights of women," *Marriage Hygiene*, 4:30–33, 1937.

BLANCHARD, PHYLLIS. "Sex in the adolescent girl," in Calverton, V. F., and Schmalhausen, S. D., ed., *Sex in civilization*, 1929, pp. 538–561.

BOAS, C. V. E. "Group therapy of anorgastic women," *Int. J. Sexol.*, 1950, 4:1–6.

BONAPARTE, M. "Les deux frigidités de la femme," *Bull. de la Soc. de Sexol.*, No. 5, 1933.

—— "Passivity, masochism and femininity," *Int. J. Psychoanal.*, 16:325–333, 1935.

—— "De l'angoisse devant la sexualité," *Revue française de psychoanalyse*, No. 4, 1948.

CALVERTON, V. F., and SCHMALHAUSEN, S. D., ed. *Sex in civilization.* New York: Macaulay, 1929.

CHESSER, EUSTACE. *The sexual, marital and family relationships of the English woman.* London: Hutchinson's Medical Publications, 1956.

COLLEY, THOMAS. "The nature and origins of psychological sexual identity," *Psychological Review*, 66:165–177, 1959.

CORNSWEET, A. C. and HAYES, M. F. "Conditioned response to fellatio," *Amer. J. Psychiatry*, 103:76–78, 1946.

CURRAN, F. J. and LEVINE, MATTHEW. "A body image study of prostitutes," *J. Crim. Psychopathy*, 4:93–116, 1942.

CURRAN, F. J., STRAUSS, B. V., and VOGEL, B. F. "Group sex conferences as a diagnostic, therapeutic and pedagogic method," *J. Crim. Psychopathy*, 5:289–300, 1943.

DALY, C. D. "The menstruation complex in literature," *Psychol. Quarterly*, 4:307–340, 1935.

DAVID, LESTER. "British 'Kinsey Report' reveals: How American-British women compare," *Coronet*, Aug. 1957.

DAVIS, KATHERINE, B. *Factors in the sex life of twenty-two hundred women.* New York & London: Harper, 1929.

DAVIS, MAXINE. *The sexual responsibility of women.* New York: Dial, 1956.

DEUTSCH, HELENE. "Homosexuality in women," *Int. J. Psychoanal.*, 14:34:56, 1933. (Orthodox psychoanalytic point of view.)

—— *The psychology of women. A psychoanalytic interpretation.* New York: Grune & Stratton, 1944–45.

DICKINSON, R. L. *Human sex anatomy.* Baltimore: Williams and Wilkins, 1933.

—— *The doctor as marriage counselor*, unpublished ms., 1940, Chap. 16, "Autoerotism."

—— *Human sex anatomy. A topographical hand atlas.* Baltimore: Williams & Wilkins Co., 1949.

DICKINSON, R. L., and BEAM, L. *A thousand marriages. A medical study of sex adjustment.* Baltimore: Williams &. Wilkins Co., 1931.

—— *The single woman. A medical study in sex education.* Baltimore: Williams & Wilkins Co., 1934.

DINGWALL, E. J. *The girdle of chastity.* London: Routledge & Keagan Paul, 1939.

DU BOIS, CORA. *The people of Alor. A social-psychological study of an East Indian Island.* Minneapolis: University of Minnesota Press, 1944.

DUDLEY, G. A. "A rare case of female fetishism," *Inter. J. Sexol.,* v. VIII, No. 2, Nov. 1949.

EHRMANN, W. W. "Non-conformance of male and female reports in pre-marital coitus," *Soc. Problems,* 1:155–159, 1953–54.

ELLIS, ALBERT. *The folklore of sex.* New York: Grove Press, 1961.

ELLIS, ALBERT, and ABARBAMEL, A. *Encyclopedia of sexual behavior.* New York: Hawthorne Books, 1961.

ELLIS, HAVELOCK. *Studies in the psychology of sex.* (6 v.) New York: Random House, 1936.

ELKAN, E. "Evolution of female orgastic ability—a biological survey," *Inter. J. Sexol.* v. 2, No. 2, Nov. 1942.

ELWIN, V. *The Muria and their ghotul.* Bombay: Geoffrey Cumberlege, Oxford University Press, 1947. (Excellent for comparative sex mores and mating patterns among adolescents in a "free" primitive society.)

FACTOR, MORRIS. "A woman's psychological reaction to attempted rape," *Psychoanal. Quart.,* 23:243–244, 1954.

FELDMAN, S. "Anxiety and orgasm," *Yearbook of Psychoanalysis,* 8:172–189, 1952.

FERENCZI, S. (Bunker, H. A., trans.) "Male and female: Psychoanalytic reflections on the 'theory of genitality,' and on secondary and tertiary sex differences," *Psychoanal. Quart.* 5:249–260, 1936.

FERGUSON, L. W. "Correlates of woman's orgasm," *J. Psychol.,* 6:295–302, 1938.

FINK, L. A. "Premarital sex experience of girls in Sidney: a survey of 100 girls," *Int. J. Sexol.,* 4:33–35, 1950.

FLUEGEL, J. C. "On the biological basis of sexual repression and its sociological significance," *The Brit. J. Psychol.* (Med. Sect'n), v. 1, Parts 3 & 4, 1921.

FORD, C. S. and BEACH, F. A. *Patterns of sexual behavior.* New York: Harper and Hoeber, 1951.

FORESTER, DORA. *Sex radicalism as seen by an emancipated woman of the new time.* Chicago: M. Harman, 1905.

FOULKES, S. H. "The idea of a change of sex in women," *Inter. J. Psychoanal.*, 24:53–56, 1943.

FRANZBLAU, ABRAHAM N. *The road to sexual maturity.* New York: Simon & Schuster, 1954.

FREED, S. C. and KROGER, W. S. "Psychological manifestations of the menstrual cycle," *Psychosomatic Medicine*, 12:229–235, 1950.

Freud, S. "Letter to Dr. F. S. Krauss," *Anthropophyteia*, 7:472–474, 1910.

—— (Brill, A. A. trans.) *Three contributions to the sexual theory.* New York: J. Nervous & Mental Disease Publishing Co., 1910.

—— (Paul, E. and C., trans.) Preface to *A young girl's diary.* New York: Thomas Seltzer, 1921.

—— (Riviere, J., and Strachey, A. and J., trans.) *Collected Papers.* (4 v.) London: Hogarth Press and Institute of Psychoanalysis, 1924.

—— "Some psychological consequences of the anatomical distinction between the sexes," *Intern. J. Psychoanal.*, 8:133–142, 1927.

—— "Female sexuality," *Intern. J. Psychoanal.*, 13:281–297, 1932.

—— (Sprott, W. J. H., trans.) *New introductory lectures on psychoanalysis.* New York: W. W. Norton, 1933.

—— (Riviere, J. trans.) *A general introduction to psychoanalysis.* New York: Perma Giants, 1935.

—— (Brill, A. A. ed.) *The basic writings of Sigmund Freud.* New York: Modern Library, 1938.

—— (Strachey, J. trans.) *An outline of psychoanalysis.* New York: W. W. Norton, 1949.

—— (Strachey, J. trans. and ed.) *Collected Papers*, Volume V. London: Hogarth Press and Institute of Psychoanalysis, 1950.

FRIED, EDRITA. *The ego in love and sexuality.* New York: Grune & Stratton, 1960.

FROMM, E. "Sex and character," *Psychiatry* 6:1 (Feb.), 1943.

GLUECK, S. and GLUECK, E. T. *Five hundred delinquent women.* New York: Alfred A. Knopf, 1934.

GOITEIN, P. L. "The potential prostitute: the role of anorexia in the defense against prostitution desires," *J. Crim. Psychopathol.*, 3:359–367, 1942.

GOLDSCHMIDT, THEA. "The menstrual taboo and woman's psychology," *J. Abn. & Socl. Psychol.*, 29:218–221, 1934.

GOUGH, E. KATHLEEN. "Female initiation rites on the Malabar Coast," *J. of the Royal Anthropological Inst.*, 85:45–80, 1955.

GRAFENBERG, E. "The role of the urethra in female orgasm," *Int. J. Sexol.* 3:145–148, 1950.

GRAHAM, S. R. "The effects of psychoanalytically oriented psychotherapy in levels of frequency and satisfaction in sexual activity," *J. Clin. Psychol.*, 16:94–95, 1960.

GREENACRE, PHYLLIS. "The pre-puberty trauma in girls," *Yearbook of Psychoanal.*, 7:159–174, 1951.

——— "Special problems of early female sexual development," In *Psychoanal. Study of the Child*, v. 6. New York: Int. Univ. Pr.

GUYON, R. *Études d'éthique sexuelle* (6 v.). St. Denis, Dardaillon & Dardaillon & Dagnieux, 1929–38. (Highly important philos. study.)

——— (Fluegel, J. C. and Ingeborg, trans.) *Sex life and sex ethics*. London: John Lane, 1933.

——— *The ethics of sexual acts*. New York: A. A. Knopf, 1948.

HAMBLIN, R. L. and BLOOD, R. O. "Pre-marital experiences and the wife's sexual adjustment," *Social Problems*, 4:122–130, 1956–57.

HARDENBERGH, E. W. "The psychology of feminine sex experience," *Int. J. Sexol.* 2:224–228, 1949.

HART, RUTH D'ARCY. "Monthly rhythm of libido in married women," *Brit. Med. J.* No. 5178:1023–24, 1960.

HARTSHORNE, EMILY. *The practice of marriage counseling*. New York: Association Press, 1951.

HASNAT, ABUL. *Sex, love, and happy marriage*. Calcutta: Standard Publisher, 1951.

HEINE, MAURICE. *Recueil de confessions et observations psycho-sexuelles*. Paris: Terrain Vague, 1957.

HORNEY, KAREN. "The dread of women. Observations in a specific difference in the dread felt by men and by women respectively for the opposite sex," *Intern. J. Psychoanal.*, 13:348–360, 1932.

HUSBAND, R. W. "Sex difference in dream contents," *J. Abnormal & Socl. Psych.* 30:513–521, 1936.

JONES, ERNEST. "The early development of female sexuality," *Intern. J. Psychoanal.*, 8:459–472, 1927.

KANIN, E. J. and HOWARD, D. H. "Post-marital consequences of pre-marital sex adjustment," *Amer. Sociol. Rev.*, 23:556–562, 1958.

KANZER, Mark. "Observations on blank dreams with orgasm," *Psychoanal. Quart.*, 23:511–520, 1954.

KAREN, R. L. "Some variables affecting sexual attitudes, behavior and inconsistence," *Marriage and Family Living*, 21:235–239, 1959.

KEISER, SYLVIA. "A manifest Oedipus Complex in an adolescent girl," *Psychoanal. Study of the Child*, 8:99–107, 1953.

KELLY, G. I. *Sexual feeling in woman.* Elkay Co.: Augusta, Ga., 1930. (Much interesting material.)

KIKI. (Putnam, S., trans., Hemingway, Ernest, Introd.), *Kiki's memoirs.* Paris: Edward W. Titus, 1930.

Kinsey, A. C. et al. 1949. Concepts of normality and abnormality in sexual behavior. In: Hoch, P. H. and Zubin, J., ed. Psychosexual development in health and disease, pp. 11–32.

—— 1953. Sexual behavior in the human female. Philadelphia and London, W. B. Saunders Co.

KLEIN, VIOLA. "The psychology of women; a critique of the theories of Helene Deutsch," *Complex* No. 3:26–43.

KLUMBIES, G. and KLEINSORGE, H. "Circulatory dangers and prophylaxis during orgasm," *Int. J. Sexol.*, 4:61–66, 1950.

KNIGHT, R. P. "Functional disturbances in the sexual life of women. Frigidity and related disorders," *Bull. Menninger Clin.* 25–35, 1943.

KRAFFT-EBING, R. VON. (Rebman, F. J. trans.). *Psychopathia sexualis, etc.* Brooklyn, N.Y.: Physicians &. Surgeons Book Co., 1922.

KRAMER, PAUL. "Early capacity for orgastic discharge," in *Psychoanal. Study of the Child*, v. IX, 1954.

KRANTZ, K. E. "Innervation of the human vulva and vagina," *J. Obst. and Gynecol.*, Oct., 1958.

KRAUSS, F. S. and SATOW, TAMIO. (Ihm, Hermann, ed. and trans.) *Japanisches Geschlechtsleben.* Leipzig: "Anthropophyteia" Verlag fuer Urtriebkunde, 1931.

KROGER, W. S. and FREED, S. C. "Psychosomatic aspects of frigidity," *J. Amer. Med. Assoc.* 143:526–532, 1950.

KRONHAUSEN, E. and KRONHAUSEN, P. *Pornography and the law.* New York: Ballantine Books, Inc., 1959.

—— 1960. Sex histories of American college men. New York: Ballantine Books, Inc.

LAMPL-DEGROOT, J. "On masturbation and its influence on general development," *Psychoanal. study of the child*, 5:153–174, 1950.

—— "On the problem of feminity," *Inter. J. Psychoanal.*, 15:314–317, 1934.

LAMSON, HERBERT D. "Human 'She-Wolves,'" *Inter. J. Sexol.* v. 6, No. 3, Feb. 1953, pp. 168–171.

LANDIS, C. et al. *Sex in development.* New York & London: Paul B. Hoeber, 1940. (Psychol. & med. considerations on comparative groups of normal & disturbed women.)

LANDIS, CARNEY and BOLLES, E. M. *Personality and sexuality of the physically handicapped woman.* New York: Hoeber, 1942.

LANVAL, MARC. "General anaesthesia and sexual frigidity," *Marriage Hygiene*, 1:236–237, 1948.

LAWRENCE, JOHN. *The single woman.* New York: Duell, Sloan and Pearce, 1952.

LAZARSFELD, SOFIE, and KADIS, ASYA. "Change of life—end of life?" *J. Indiv. Psychol.*, 14:167–170, 1958.

LEHFELDT, HANS and ELLIS, ALBERT (eds.). Aspects of female sexuality. "Monograph of the Society for the Scientific Study of Sex." *Quarterly Rev. Surgery, Obst. & Gynecol.*, 16:217–263, 1959.

LEVINE, LENA. "A criteria for orgasm in the female," *Inter. J. Sexol.*, 1:173–174, 1948.

LICHT, H. (Freese, J. H., trans.). *Sexual life in ancient Greece.* London: Geo. Routledge &. Sons, 1932. (Most authoritative study to date.)

LORAND, SANDOR. "Contributions to the problem of vaginal orgasm," *Inter. J. Psychoanal.*, 20:432–438, 1939.

LYNN, D. B. "A note on the sex difference in the development of male and female identification," *Psychoanal. Rev.*, 66:126–135, 1959.

MALINOWSKI, B. *The sexual life of savages in Northwestern Melanesia.* New York: Halcyon House, 1928.

MALLESON, JOAN. "The psychology of feminine sex experience," *Inter. J. Sexol.*, 11:255, 1949.

MARMOR, JUDD. "Some considerations concerning orgasm in the female," *Psychosom. Med.*, 16:3, 1954.

MASLOW, A. H. "Self-esteem (dominance feeling) and sexuality in women," *J. Socl. Psychol.*, 16:259–294, 1942.

MASTERS, WILLIAM H. "The sexual response cycle of the human female: vaginal lubrication," *Annals of the New York Academy of Sciences*, v. 83, Article 2, pp. 301–317, 1959.

—— "The sexual response cycle of the human female. I. Gross

anatomic considerations," *Western J. Surgery, Obst., & Gynecol.*, 68:57–72, 1960.

MASTERS, WILLIAM H. and JOHNSON, VIRGINIA E. *The human female: anatomy of sexual response.* Minnesota Medicine, v. 43: 31–36, 1960.

—— "Orgasm-anatomy of the female," in Ellis, A., and Abarbamel, A., *Encyclopedia of sexual behavior.* New York: Hawthorne Books, 1961.

MCCARTNEY, J. L. "Paradise lost: the psychology of the Marshall Islanders," *J. Clin. Psychopathol.*, 16:259–294, 1947.

MEAD, M. *From the South-Seas. Studies of adolescence and sex in primitive societies.* New York: William Morrow &. Co., 1939.

—— *Male and female. A study of the sexes in a changing world.* New York: William Morrow & Co., 1949.

MILLER, M. M., and ROBINSON, D. M., trans. and ed. *The songs of Sappho, including the recent Egyptian discoveries. The poems of Erinna. Greek poems about Sappho. Ovid's epistle of Sappho to Phaon.* Lexington, Ky.: Maxwelton Co., 1925.

MONTAGU, M. F., ASHLEY. *Coming into being among the Australian Aborigines.* London: George Routledge &. Sons, 1937.

MORENO, J. L. "Group psychotherapy, psychodrama and the warming up process to the sexual act," *Inter. J. Sexol.*, 8:12–15.

NEEDLES, W. "A note on orgastic loss of consciousness," *Psychoanal. Quart.*, 22:512–518.

PALM, ROSE, and ABRAHAMSEN, D. "A Rorschach study of the wives of sex offenders," *J. Nerv. & Ment. Disease*, v. 119, No. 2, pp. 167–172, 1954.

PLATTNER, KARL. *Eros im Zuchthaus.* (Eros in the penitentiary.) Hannover: Paul Witte, 1929–30. (Fascinating account of female sex aggressiveness under conditions of deprivation.)

PLOOG, PAUL D. and ROBINSON, B. W. "Experiments on localization of genital function in the brain," *Transactions, Amer. Neurol. Assoc.*, pp. 105–109, 1959.

POWDERMAKER, H. *Life in Lesu. The study of a Melanesian society in New Ireland.* New York: W. W. Norton &. Co., 1933.

REICH, W. *The discovery of the orgone; vol. 1: The function of the orgasm.* New York: Orgone Inst. Press, 1942. (Important for understanding psychophysiological release function of orgasm, in spite of contamination with unproven "orgone" theory.)

—— *The sexual revolution. Toward a self-governing character structure.* New York: Orgone Inst. Press, 1945. (Significant philosophical contribution to the problem of sexual freedom in relation to ethics and mental hygiene.)

ROSENTHAL, H. C. "Sex habits of European women vs. American women. A digest of two important new surveys," *Pageant Mag.*, March, 1951, pp. 52–59.

SCHMIDEBERG, MELITTA. "Some unconscious mechanisms in pathol. sexuality etc.," *Inter. J. Psychoanal.*, 14:225–260, 1933.

SHOR, JOEL. "Female sexuality; aspects and prospects," *Psychoanalysis*, II:3, pp. 47–76, 1954. (A psychoanalytic interpretation of mutal orgasm.)

STEKEL, W. (Van Teslaar, J. S., trans.) *Frigidity in women.* New York: Grove Press, 2 v., 1962.

STEPHENS, A. O. "Premarital sex relationships," in Fishbein, M., & Burgess, E. W. ed. *Successful Marriage*, 1947.

STONE, ABRAHAM, and STONE, HANNAH. *A marriage manual.* New York: Simon & Schuster, 1952.

STRAKOSCH, F. M. *Factors in the sex life of seven hundred psychopathic women.* Utica, N.Y.: State Hospitals Press, 1934.

TANIZAKI, JUNICHIRO (Howard Hibbett, trans.). *The Key.* New York: Alfred A. Knopf, 1961.

TANNENBAUM, S. A. "Orgasm in the female," *J. Sexol. & Psychoanal.* 2:31–36, 1924.

TERMAN, L. M. "Correlates of orgasm adequacy in a group of 556 wives," *J. Psychol.* 32:115–172, 1951.

THOMPSON, CLARA. "The role of women in this culture," *Psychiatry*, v. 4, No. 1, 1941.

—— "Towards a psychology of women," *Pastoral Psychol.*, May, 1953.

VAN DE VELDE, T. H. *Ideal Marriage.* New York: Covici Friede, 1930.

—— *Sex Hostility in marriage.* London: Wm. Heinemann, 1931.

VAN GULIK, R. H. *Erotic color prints of the Ming period, with an essay on Chinese sex life from the Han to the Ch'ing*

Dynasty, B.C. *206*–A.D. *1644*. Tokyo: priv. print., 3v. + illus., 1952.

VIGMAN, F. K. "Sexual precocity of young girls in the United States," *Int. J. Sexol.* 6:90–91, 1952.

WALLIN, P. "Marital satisfaction and husbands' and wives' perception of similarity in their preferred frequency of coitus," *J. Abn. Soc. Psychol.* 57:370–373, 1958.

WESTERMAN, HOLSTIJN, A. J. *Les organes génitaux féminins; l'orgasm et la frigidité*. Unpublished ms., 1960. (A psychoanalytic interpretation.)

WITMER, HELEN L. *The attitudes of mothers toward sex education*. Minneapolis, Minn.: The Univ. of Minn. Press, 1929.

WYLIE, PHILIP. "Psychology of women," *Psychoanalysis*, 1:7–23, 1953.